A.B. McCullough

The Commercial Fishery of the Canadian Great Lakes

**Studies in Archaeology
Architecture and History**

**National Historic Parks and Sites
Canadian Parks Service
Environment Canada**

©Minister of Supply and Services Canada 1989.

Available in Canada through authorized bookstore agents and other bookstores, or by mail from the Canadian Government Publishing Centre, Supply and Services Canada, Hull, Quebec, Canada K1A 0S9.

Published under the authority
of the Minister of the Environment,
Ottawa, 1989

Editing and design: Jean Brathwaite

Parks publishes the results of its research in archaeology, architecture, and history. A list of publications is available from Research Publications, Canadian Parks Service, Environment Canada, 1600 Liverpool Court, Ottawa, Ontario K1A 0H3.

Canadian Cataloguing in Publication Data

McCullough, A.B. (Alan Bruce), 1945–

The commercial fishery of the Canadian Great Lakes

(Studies in archaeology, architecture and history,
ISSN 0821-1027)
Issued also in French under title: La pêche commerciale dans le secteur canadien des Grands Lacs.
Includes bibliographical references.
ISBN 0-660-12937-X
DSS cat. no. R61-2/9-40E

1. Fisheries — Great Lakes — History. 2. Great Lakes. I. Canada. National Historic Parks and Sites. II. Title. III. Series.

SH219.6M33 1988   C88-097036-7   639.21'09713

Cover   Fishermen on the Bay of Quinte, ca. 1911.
Ontario. Game and Fisheries Dept., *Fifth Annual Report ... 1911* (Toronto: L.K. Cameron, King's Printer, 1912), facing p. 10; National Library of Canada, NL 13105.

Contents

Preface

Commercial fishing is the oldest and one of the most important of Canada's resource-based industries. The fisheries comprise three major sectors: the saltwater Atlantic and Pacific fisheries of roughly equal importance and the smaller, but still significant, freshwater fishery. The freshwater fishery may be divided into a number of regional fisheries of which the most important is the Great Lakes fishery.

Commercial fishing on the Great Lakes began about 1800, and by 1900 it had become an important regional industry. Despite many crises, changes in the fish populations in the lakes, environmental degradation, technological innovations, and changes in economic organization, the fishery remains a viable industry today.

In 1983–84 the Historical Research Branch of the National Historic Parks and Sites Directorate, Canadian Parks Service, Department of the Environment, prepared a study of commercial fishing on the Great Lakes for the Systems Planning Unit of the directorate. The study was to provide information on the basis of which the Historic Sites and Monuments Board of Canada could assess the national historic significance of the Great Lakes fishery. The study is available in the Parks Service's Microfiche Report Series, No. 305, as "The Commercial Fisheries of the Canadian Great Lakes: A Systems Plan Thematic Study." The present work consists of the historical section of the study. It is published as a brief synthesis of the scientific, economic, and historical literature on the fishery. It also adds to a growing body of short studies of Canadian fisheries published by Parks:
B.A. Balcom, *The Cod Fishery of Isle Royale, 1713–58* (1984);
Roch Samson, *Fishermen and Merchants in 19th Century Gaspé; The Fishermen-Dealers of William Hyman and Sons* (1984);
Jean-Pierre Proulx, *Whaling in the North Atlantic from Earliest Times to the Mid-19th Century* (1986); and

James E. Candow, *Of Men and Seals: A History of the Newfoundland Seal Hunt* (1989).

A note on style may be useful. For the sake of simplicity the political and geographic designation *Ontario* has been used for Upper Canada, 1791–1841, Canada West, 1841–1867, and Ontario, 1867 to the present. In spelling compound words such as *gill net*, *hoop net*, and *trap net* I have followed standard practice, although local usage favours *gillnet*, *hoopnet*, and *trapnet*. I have used common rather than scientific names for fishes, following the usage suggested in the American Fisheries Society's *List of Common and Scientific Names of Fishes from the United States and Canada*, 4th edition (Bethseda, Maryland: 1980), and W.B. Scott and E.J. Crossman, *Freshwater Fishes of Canada* (Ottawa: Fisheries Research Board of Canada, 1973).

I wish to thank Gordon Bennett of the Canadian Parks Service, Environment Canada; W. Jack Christie, Great Lakes Coordinator, Ontario Ministry of Natural Resources; and Duncan Stacey, Vancouver, B.C., for reading and commenting on the manuscript. I also with to thank J. Tilt, Commercial Development Coordinator, Fisheries Branch, Ontario Ministry of Natural Resources, for his assistance, and my editor, Jean Brathwaite, for her attention to detail and for attempting to show me the difference between restrictive and non-restrictive relative clauses.

I alone, of course, am responsible for the opinions expressed in this book and for any errors it contains.

Submitted for publication 1985, by A.B. McCullough, Historical Research Branch, National Historic Parks and Sites Directorate, Ottawa.

Introduction

During the nineteenth century the Great Lakes supported the largest freshwater fishery in the world. Today as a result of intensive fishing and environmental changes the fishery is very different from what it was a century ago, but it remains one of the world's largest freshwater fisheries. The fishery is shared by Canada and the United States; in the nineteenth century about 20 per cent of the catch was from Canadian waters, now about 40 per cent of the catch is Canadian. Traditionally the Great Lakes have produced almost 50 per cent (by value) of all freshwater fish produced in Canada; today, as a result of increased catches in other inland waters and lower unit values for Great Lakes fish, only about one-third of freshwater fish come from the Great Lakes. In comparison with sea fisheries the Great Lakes fishery is much less significant; for example, over the past century the Nova Scotia fishery has been five to six times more valuable than the Ontario fishery.[1] The Ontario fishery is also much less valuable than those of Newfoundland, New Brunswick, and British Columbia; it has been roughly equal in value to those of Quebec and Prince Edward Island.

This paper examines the history of the commercial fishery on the Canadian Great Lakes, emphasizing the development and interaction of three major themes: technological change, economic organization, and resource management. A commercial fishery is defined as one in which fish are caught almost exclusively for sale in contrast to a subsistence fishery or a sports fishery. A subsistence fishery is one in which most fish are consumed by the fisherman, his family, band (in the case of Indian fisheries), or employer (in the case of fishermen employed to provision a specific commercial or military establishment). A sport fishery is one in which fish are caught for pleasure. There are, of course, many commercial aspects to the

1 The Goderich fishing fleet, 1884.

Ontario. Dept. of Fisheries, *Fifth Annual Report ... 1903* (Toronto: L.K. Cameron, King's Printer, 1904), p. ii; National Library of Canada, NL 13100.

sport-fishing industry, and some commercial fishermen are also involved in the sport-fishing industry, but essentially commercial fishing and sport fishing are different and often antagonistic.

Background

The Great Lakes of North America constitute the largest lake system in the world. Lake Superior, with an area of 31 820 square miles, is the world's largest freshwater lake. Lake Huron (23 010 square miles), Lake Michigan (22 400 square miles), Lake Erie (9940 square miles), and Lake Ontario (7540 square miles) rank fourth, fifth, eleventh, and thirteenth respectively. The lakes, excepting Lake Michigan, form the boundary between Canada and the United States; about 47 per cent of the total area of the four boundary lakes lies in Canada. In the seventeenth century when Europeans first visited them, they supported an immense population of fish made up of over 150 species including most of the varieties that have been the basis of the commercial fishing industry: whitefish, lake trout, sturgeon, pike, perch, and lake herring or cisco.

The potential always existed for a large commercial fishery on the Great Lakes, but its development awaited either the growth of a large local market or a means to transport fish to a large external market. There was a substantial Indian population on the shores of the Great Lakes at the time of the lakes' discovery by Europeans, and the Indians made extensive use of the fish resources of the area.[1] Some lakeshore tribes, such as the Ojibwa in the vicinity of Sault Ste. Marie, traded dried fish to inland tribes,[2] but in general, Indian fisheries were subsistence fisheries. During the late eighteenth and early nineteenth centuries several small European settlements were made on the lakes, notably at Niagara-on-the-Lake, Detroit, Michilimackinac (on the Straits of Mackinac), and Fort William. People at these settlements fished or employed fishermen, but the fisheries continued to be essentially subsistence in nature.

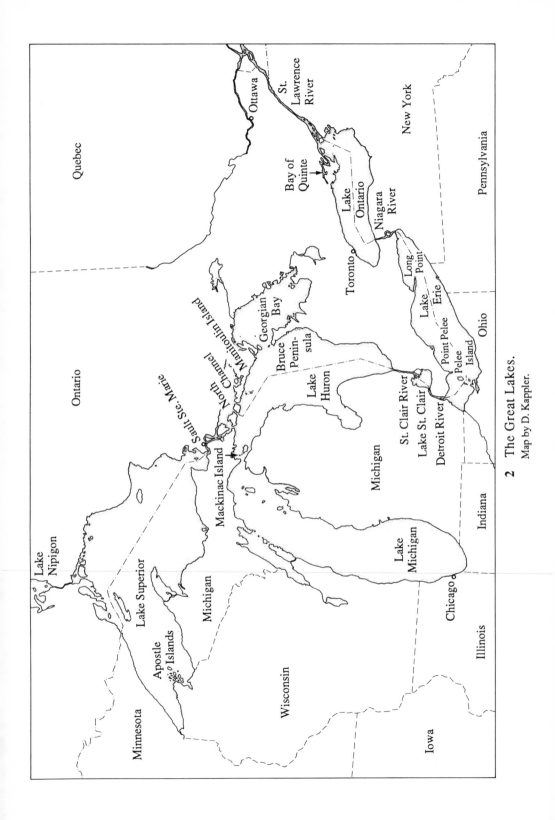

2 The Great Lakes.
Map by D. Kappler.

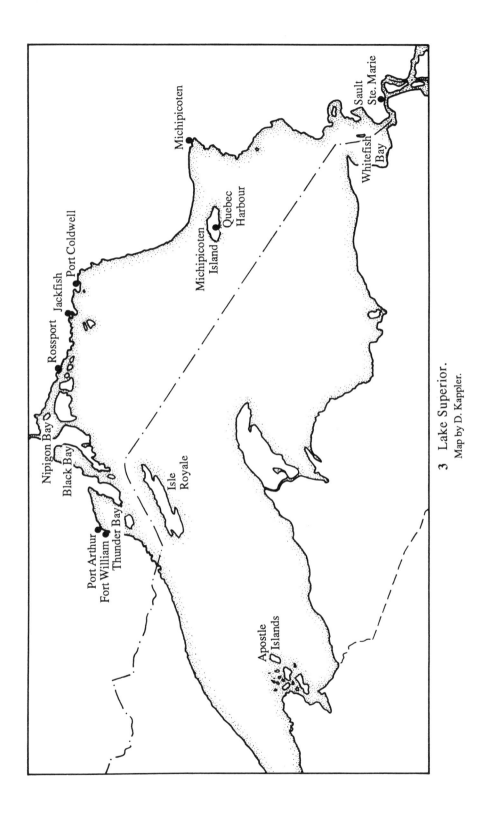

3 Lake Superior.
Map by D. Kappler.

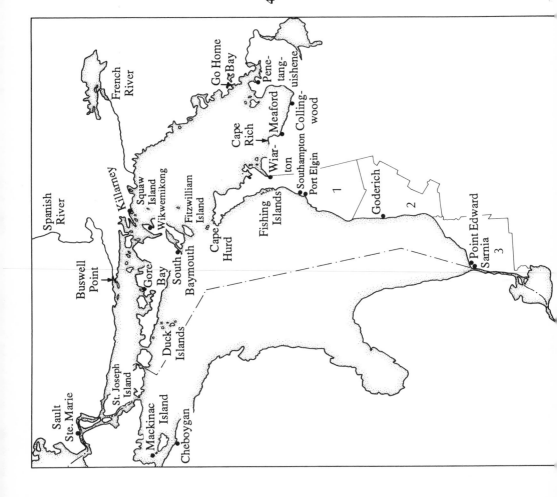

4 Lake Huron. *1*, Bruce; *2*, Huron; and *3*, Lambton counties. Map by D. Kappler.

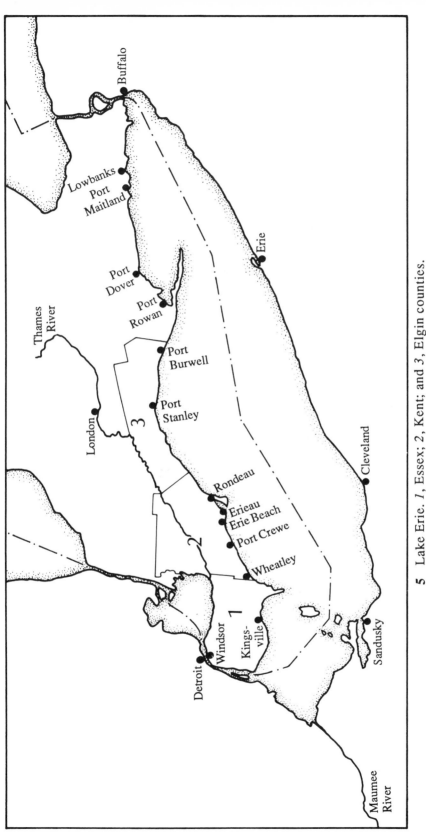

5 Lake Erie. *1*, Essex; *2*, Kent; and *3*, Elgin counties.

Map by D. Kappler.

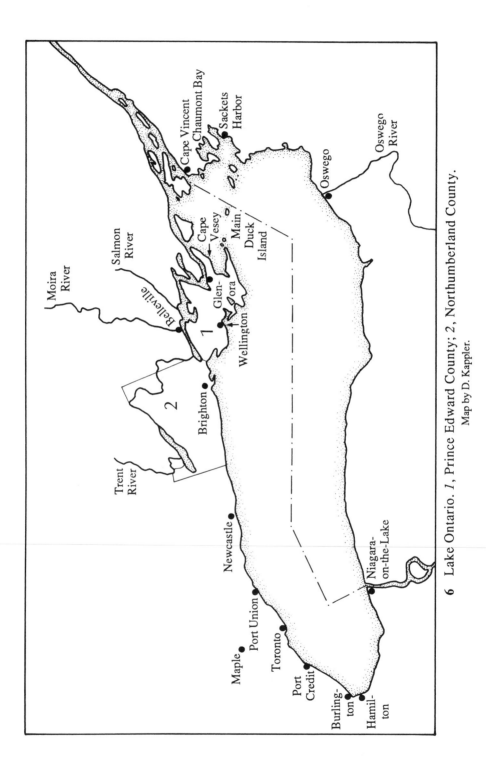

6 Lake Ontario. *1*, Prince Edward County; *2*, Northumberland County.
Map by D. Kappler.

Large-scale European settlement on the shores of the Great Lakes did not begin until after the American Revolution. In 1791 the population of Ontario was estimated at 50 000 people, but by 1851 it was 952 004.[3] With settlement the scale of fishing increased, but when and where subsistence fishing first became commercial fishing is not clear. There are references to commercial fishing in Burlington Bay and on the Pennsylvania shore of Lake Erie in the 1790s,[4] but it is generally agreed that the first commercial fisheries on the Great Lakes were established on the American side of Lake Ontario in Chaumont Bay, near the Maumee River on Lake Erie, and on the Detroit River at about the time of the War of 1812.[5] With the exception of the reference to a fishery in Burlington Bay in the 1790s, there is little evidence of a commercial fishery on the Canadian shores of the lakes until the 1820s and 1830s. However, the existence of large-scale fisheries, whether subsistence, commercial, or sport, may be inferred from the existence of legislation to protect salmon in Lake Ontario (1807), herring in Burlington Bay (1823), whitefish in the Niagara, Detroit, and St. Clair rivers (1833), and lake trout in Lake Erie (1843).

By the mid-1830s there was a commercial fishery on the Toronto Islands of sufficient importance that the city council passed bylaws regulating it.[6] A decade later 150 to 200 men were employed in a whitefish and salmon fishery in the vicinity of Weller's Beach in Prince Edward County.[7] Salt fish were exported to the United States from the Pelee area of Lake Erie from as early as 1824,[8] but nothing further is known about the Lake Erie fishery until the 1840s. American and Canadian fisheries on the Detroit River, Lake St. Clair, and St. Clair River system date at least to the War of 1812, when Detroit developed as a market for salt fish.

Although Lake Erie has always been an important part of the American fishery, the Canadian Lake Erie fishery was later in developing than the fisheries on Lakes Ontario and Huron. Before 1900 the Lake Huron fishery was more valuable than that of Lake Erie. The Ojibwa fishery at Sault Ste. Marie was of great antiquity and had some characteristics of a commercial fishery even before European contact. The commercial aspects of the Sault fishery were accentuated after the arrival of Europeans. In 1807–08 the Askin family exported small quantities of salted whitefish in barrels from the Sault, or St. Joseph Island, to Detroit.[9] When J. Bigsby, a geologist with the international boundary commission, visited the Sault in 1822 he found that the catching of whitefish for export employed several villages.[10] In 1839 the novelist Captain Frederick Marryat described a thriving fishery at Mackinac and Sault Ste. Marie.[11] Although Marryat noted that there was no fishery on the Canadian shore of the Sault, several fisheries were established on the Canadian shores of Lake Huron in the 1830s. From about 1831 Alexander McGregor of Goderich operated a fishery at the Fishing Islands north of Southampton. In 1834 he had a contract to deliver 3 000 barrels of fish annually to Detroit.[12] A New Yorker, John P. Slocum, established a fishery at Point Edward in 1838. There was also a small fishery at Penetanguishene in the 1830s, but whether or not it was a commercial operation is unclear.[13]

A commercial fishery developed on Lake Superior almost as early as on the other lakes. American fishermen became interested in Lake Superior about 1830, and in 1836 the American Fur Company began a commercial operation on the lake. Its base was in the Apostle Islands, but it fished on both sides of the lake. In 1838 and 1839 it shipped 4000 and 4800 barrels of fish. Although the company went bankrupt in 1842, smaller operations continued in business on Lake Superior; 4000 barrels of fish were shipped out of the area in 1850–51.[14] On the Canadian side of the lake the Hudson's Bay Company and earlier fur-trading companies employed fishermen to provision their posts; in 1826–27 the staff at Fort William consumed 20 000 pounds of salt fish and 7500 fresh fish.[15] In 1835–36 the company began to ship salted whitefish and lake trout from its posts at Fort William, Michipicoten, and Sault Ste. Marie to Detroit. The Hudson's Bay Company fishery was on a smaller scale than the American Fur Company's, but it continued into the 1860s, by which time independent Canadian fishermen had appeared on Lake Superior.[16]

By the 1850s commercial fishing on the Great Lakes in Ontario was well established, albeit on a small scale. The 1851 census reported that 11 886 barrels of fish, probably equal to 2 377 200 pounds, had been cured in the province by 96 fishermen.[17] The census made no mention of fresh fish although they were sold in local markets and in some cases exported. The fish-curing industry was concentrated at the eastern end of Lake Ontario, in Prince Edward and Northumberland counties, where about 50 per cent of all cured fish were produced. Twenty-five per cent were produced in Bruce and Huron counties on Lake Huron and about 8 per cent were produced in Kent, Lambton, and Essex counties on Lakes Huron and Erie and the Detroit and St. Clair rivers. In 1857 the Ontario fisheries superintendent reported that the total value of the fisheries in Lakes Ontario, Huron, and Erie was over $468 000; of this almost $180 000 worth came from the fresh-fish operations of Port Credit, Port Union, and Toronto.[18]

Although the fishery in the first half of the nineteenth century was small by subsequent standards, it was sufficiently large, in combination with environmental changes such as the damming of spawning streams, to affect fish stocks in areas where it was concentrated. As early as 1840, salmon were less common in some of their spawning rivers than they had been. In 1857 the superintendent of fisheries in Ontario reported that salmon had long since disappeared from the Moira, Trent, and Salmon rivers and that what had once been a major salmon fishery at Main Duck Island on Lake Ontario was greatly reduced.[19]

Pre-Confederation Legislation and Regulations

The legislature of Ontario passed its first fishery protection legislation, "An Act for the Preservation of the Salmon," in 1807. The act forbade the taking of salmon orsalmon fry with nets or weirs in rivers or creeks in the Newcastle and Home districts. (These districts extended along the north shore of Lake Ontario from Hamilton to Prince Edward County.) It did not prevent the use of spears or hooks and lines. Three years later the act was amended to prevent the taking of salmon by any means from 25 October to 1 January and to prohibit the taking of salmon within 100 yards of any mill or milldam at any time.[1] The act and its amendment established three of the principles that continue to govern fishery conservation laws in the Great Lakes today. First, the government could regulate the types of gear used in fishing. Second, it could regulate where fishing could take place. Third, it could establish closed seasons during which all fishing was banned; usually these seasons were designed to protect the fish during spawning. The act did not provide for the appointment of any officials to enforce it; rather, informers were encouraged by the promise of one-half of any fines collected. It was to be another 50 years before wardens were appointed, and even then enforcement remained a weak point of fishery policy because wardens were too few, too poorly equipped, or too poorly paid to enforce the regulations.

The principles governing fishery protection were expanded by an act of 1828 that required "aprons" on all milldams on streams that were frequented by salmon and perch or that were used for running logs.[2] The description of the "apron" suggests that it was more of a timber slide than a fish ladder; nevertheless, the principle that fish must be allowed access to their spawning beds was important. The failure to enforce the principle is now considered to have been one of the causes of the extinction of salmon in Lake Ontario.[3]

In 1823 and 1836 the legislature passed laws for the protection of the herring fishery in Burlington Bay. In 1833 it gave some protection to whitefish in the Niagara, Saint Clair, and Detroit rivers. In 1843 legislation was passed to protect lake trout in Kent and Essex counties on Lake Erie.[4] In each case the legislation provided for some form of closed season, limited the types of gear that could be used, and except in the case of Lake Erie trout, limited where gear could be used. The acts were rudimentary and left the initiative for enforcement to informers; nevertheless, they extended the principles of fishery management to the three species that formed the backbone of the commercial fishery until the end of the First World War.

Another important principle of fishery management was enunciated in the Fisheries Inspection Act of 1840.[5] Although the bulk of the act, designed to ensure the quality of fish packed in Ontario, remained a dead letter, one provision, which limited the right to fish to residents of Ontario (later expanded to British subjects), became a fixed element in fishery management policy. The policy was a contentious one since the international boundary passed through many of the best fishing grounds on the Great Lakes, and the temptation for Americans to fish in Canadian waters, and vice versa, was great.

In 1857 and 1858 the Ontario government revised and consolidated its fishery legislation in one act, for the first time known by the short title "The Fishery Act."[6] The new act incorporated most of the earlier provisions for the protection of the fishery including regulation of the times, methods, and places of fishing, and the use of fish ladders. In addition it introduced four other principles of fishery management. First, the act of 1858 declared that the government could license or lease fisheries for periods of up to nine years. Prior to 1857 the Great Lakes fishery was treated as a "public right" vested in the public and not in the crown; consequently the government had not leased nor licensed fisheries. It had, however, leased or issued licences of occupation to crown lands that fronted on desirable fishing sites. In the case of a seine fishery such a licence gave effective control of the fishery to the licencee.[7] By declaring its right to lease fisheries, the government put itself in a position to limit the number of fishermen and thus to prevent overfishing. Second, the Fishery Act encouraged the artificial propagation of fish. In 1857 and 1858, experiments in hatching salmon and trout were carried out at Quebec City by the fisheries superintendent for Canada East, Richard Nettle. Ten years later a federal government fish hatchery was established at Newcastle, Ontario, and by the end of the century, hatcheries were a major element in Canada's fishery policy. Third, the act recognized the danger of pollution and prohibited the dumping of fish offal or ballast into fishing waters and prohibited the throwing of lime or chemical substances into waters inhabited by fish. Between 1839 and 1847 several acts had been passed that prohibited dumping mill wastes into navigable streams; although these acts were intended to prevent obstructions to navigation, they would also have benefited the fishery by preventing pollution.[8] In 1868 when the federal Fisheries Act was passed, it included a provision that prohibited the dumping of sawdust or mill rubbish in any stream.[9]

Perhaps the most important provision of the fishery acts of 1857–58 was the one that shifted responsibility for enforcement from informers or municipal governments to the provincial government and gave the government authority to appoint a superintendent of fisheries and fishery overseers. A superintendent was appointed in 1857; by 1866 Ontario had a superintendent, 18 fishery overseers, and a number of guardians who were appointed on a seasonal basis to supervise spawning grounds.[10]

Although the staff was small it made some progress towards implementing the Fishery Act. The staff began systematically collecting statistics that were necessary to the management of the fishery, and attempted to enforce the laws requiring fish ladders around milldams. The introduction of a licence system proved very difficult. Many fishermen assumed that they had, through long occupation, acquired title to the fisheries they occupied. At Burlington Beach at the western end of Lake Ontario and at Cape Vesey in Prince Edward County, fishermen combined and refused either to lease the fisheries or to allow anyone else to lease them. A man appointed to report on violations of the Fishery Act at Burlington Beach was severely beaten, and in 1863 Superintendent William Gibbard disappeared while investigating fishing violations at Manitoulin Island. He was presumed to have been murdered.[11]

Technological Development
Fishing Gear

The 1850s were a period of technological as well as administrative and legal innovations in the fishery. Many of the early commercial fisheries, such as those around Prince Edward County and on the Detroit River, used seine nets. The seine used on the Great Lakes was simply a long net, somewhat deeper in the centre than at the ends. Early seines were as little as 300 feet in length; they could be much longer, and seines used on the south shore of Lake Erie today are as long as 4950 feet.[1] Usually seines have small mesh so that fish will not be caught by their gills as they are in gill nets. Legislation in 1858 established the minimum mesh size as 1.5 inches square, equivalent to 3 inches extension measure, and later 2 inches extension measure became common.[2] One end of the net was fixed to the shore and the net was set in an arc, its other end landed at a point farther along the shore. The net was then drawn in to shore and the fish trapped in it were scooped out. Originally seines were drawn by men, but horses could be used, and in the twentieth century small stationary engines equipped with winches were applied to the task.

Most of the fish were sold fresh or were salted for later sale. In a system unique to the Detroit River seine fishery, fish were scooped directly from the net into a pond or pen built in the water. Fish that were surplus to immediate market needs could be held alive for weeks or months and sold during periods of scarcity and higher prices. The drawback to the system was that the fish were susceptible to disease while penned, and losses were often high.[3]

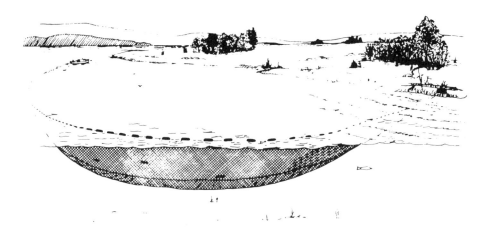

7 A seine net.

G.F. Adams and D.P. Kolenosky, *Out of the Water: Ontario's Freshwater Fish Industry* ([Toronto]: Commercial Fish and Fur Branch, Ontario Ministry of Natural Resources, 1974), p. 7.

8 Hauling in a seine on the Detroit River, ca. 1885. Fish were kept alive in the enclosure until they were marketed.

H.M. Smith and M.-M. Snell, comp., "Fisheries of the Great Lakes in 1885...," in U.S. Commission of Fish and Fisheries, *Report of the Commissioner for 1887*, USGPO, Washington, D.C., 1891, App. 1, Pl. 26.

9 Ojibwas fishing in St. Mary's Rapids at the Sault, ca. 1900.
National Archives of Canada, PA 32664.

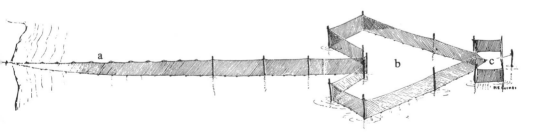

10 A pound net: *a*, leader; *b*, heart; and *c*, pot or crib. Ca. 1885.
H.M. Smith and M.-M. Snell, comp., "Fisheries of the Great Lakes in 1885...," in U.S.
Commission of Fish and Fisheries, *Report of the Commissioner for 1887*, USGPO,
Washington, D.C., 1891, App. 1, Pl. 29.

In addition to seine nets, dip nets, spears, and hooks and lines were used in the early fishery. Dip nets were used in the commercial fishery at Sault Ste. Marie and in other special situations such as the fishery on the Thames River. At the Sault two fishermen, usually Ojibwas, would paddle a canoe into the foot of the rapids. While the steersman held the canoe steady, the bowsman watched for fish in the rapids and flipped his prey into the canoe with the dip net. The skill of the Ojibwa fishermen was much admired and frequently described by European travellers.[4] Fishermen at the Sault also used spears, and spearing, particularly by torchlight, was a common method of fishing in the first half of the nineteenth century. Because many injured fish escaped to die, it was a wasteful method. In addition, spearing made fish less desirable for salting and later sale. The legislation of 1857 banned spearing of salmon, muskellunge, speckled trout, and bass except under special licence. The ban was gradually broadened to include other fish; nevertheless, commercial ice fishing using spears was permitted by special licences in shallow waters such as Burlington Bay for many years.[5]

Hook and line fishing — either setting a long line with hundreds of hooks attached to it or trolling with several lines — was practiced in the American lake trout fishery until the 1940s. Hook and line commercial fishing was less common in Canada, but the technique was used, particularly in southern Georgian Bay and along the east coast of the Bruce Peninsula. During the 1920s and 1930s some of the commercial trout trollers in Georgian Bay became part- or fulltime charter-boat operators in the sport fishery.[6] Set lines are still used for eels and channel catfish.

The seine was a relatively inflexible and primitive method of fishing. It could only be used along the shoreline, it could only be used where the lake bottom was naturally smooth or could be cleared of obstructions, and it was only economic where fish were very common. Many of the successful Canadian seine fisheries, such as those on the Detroit River and at the Fishing Islands on Lake Huron, were on spawning grounds. Seining was a seasonal occupation, particularly when it was done on spawning grounds. Seines were popular because they were relatively cheap, were safe to operate, and could make use of unskilled labour. When fish were plentiful, immense catches could be made with seines; one fisherman told the Dominion Fishery Commission (1894) that he had sometimes caught 5000 to 10 000 whitefish in a single haul of the seine at Wellington Beach in the years 1850–77.[7] On the other hand, when fish became less common, seine users were vulnerable to criticism because the nets were often used during the spawning season and because the small mesh caught and destroyed many immature fish. In addition, drawing the nets across the lake bottom was thought to destroy spawn. In the 1890s the federal government began to limit the number of seine licences issued and to prohibit seining in some areas such as the Detroit River.[8]

In the 1840s and 1850s a new method of fishing, pound (or pond) nets, was introduced on the Great Lakes, and an old method, gill nets, became more popular. Pound nets consisted of four parts: the leader, the heart or wings, the tunnel, and the pot or crib. The whole apparatus was hung from stakes or piles driven into the lake bed. The leader was a long large-mesh net that ran perpendicular to the shore. Fish swimming parallel to the shore followed the leader into deeper water. The heart was located at the end of the leader. It was a roughly heart-shaped enclosure made of net of a smaller mesh than the leader and was designed so that fish that entered it would be unlikely to escape. At the point of the heart a completely enclosed net tunnel led into the pot, which was simply a large net "box." The mesh in the leader and heart was large. Regulations in 1894 set the minimum mesh at five inches extension measure, and some fishermen used a larger-mesh leader. The mesh in the pot was smaller, about two inches extension measure.[9] Only the smallest fish could escape from two-inch mesh. Although larger meshes were experimented with so as to allow more undersized fish to escape the pot, it was found that any mesh larger than two inches led to the gilling of a large number of legal-size fish. Gilling caused the fish to drown and reduced their value; consequently, the two-inch mesh remained standard in pots. The pot was emptied as regularly as weather permitted. The fisherman simply lowered one edge of the pot, which was held above the water level by stakes, brought a large flat-bottomed boat into the pot, raised the floor of the pot so as to crowd the fish into one corner of it, and then scooped them into the boat.

Except where large numbers of fish congregate very near shore, pound nets are generally more efficient than seines. However, because of the limitations on the length of available stakes, they were not usually set in more than 50 to 80 feet of water. Because of problems in driving stakes, pound nets could not be set in stony bottoms. And they were susceptible to ice and storm damage. As a result, pound nets were usually set in late March, taken out in midsummer to be cleaned and retarred, and replaced in the water and left until early November.

Pound nets were developed in Scotland and introduced to North America in the 1830s; they may have been used on Lake Ontario at about this time. They were set at Sandusky and on Maumee Bay in Ohio about 1850, and the first nets on the Canadian shore of Lake Erie were set at Midsly Creek and Lowbanks (both at the eastern end of the lake) in 1852.[10] The shallow water

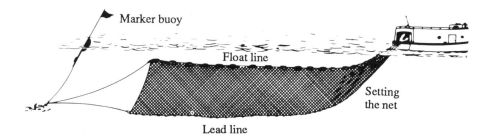

11   Setting a gill net.
G.F. Adams and D.P. Kolenosky, *Out of the Water: Ontario's Freshwater Fish Industry* ([Toronto]:
Commercial Fish and Fur Branch, Ontario Ministry of Natural Resources, 1974), p. 9.

and soft bottom of the western end of Lake Erie made it ideally suited to
pound-net fishing; more than half of all pound nets used in Canada have
been used in Lake Erie. The nets were not so popular on the other Great
Lakes. They were seldom used on the Canadian side of Lake Ontario and
were not common on the Canadian shore of Lake Huron until after 1880.[11]
They were concentrated on the southeastern shore of Lake Huron, on the
southern shore of Manitoulin Island, and in the North Channel. This concentration was a result of the nature of the coast and of a decision made in
1885 to prohibit the use of pound nets east of a line between Cape Hurd at
the tip of the Bruce Peninsula and Buswell Point at the mouth of the Spanish
River.[12] The use of pound nets on Lake Superior was restricted by the
rockiness of its shore, but a number were used in the vicinities of Whitefish
Bay, Nipigon Bay, Black Bay, and Thunder Bay. The first one was set near
Port Arthur in 1878.[13]

Gill nets are simply nets made of fine thread with sinkers attached to the
bottom of the net and floats attached to the top. As a result, although the
nets rest on the bottom, they float upright. The mesh size is varied in
accordance with the type or size of fish to be caught. For example, the 1980
fishery regulations provide a minimum mesh size of 4.5 inches for taking
lake trout, pike, yellow pickerel (walleye), and whitefish, and a minimum
mesh size of 2.25 to 3 inches, depending on the depth fished, for catching
herring or cisco.[14] Small fish can swim through the net but larger fish are
wedged and held by their gills or spiny parts. Usually a number of nets are
tied end to end to form a box; the term "box" is used because the nets are

stored in boxes before being set. A number of boxes linked together form a gang. The length of individual nets and of gangs varies from place to place and time to time as well as with the type of fish sought.

An account of fisheries on Georgian Bay in the early 1890s stated that a net made from 7.5 pounds of No. 82 cotton would be 1560 feet long and about 5 feet deep. Six of these nets would form a small gang 3120 yards long. In 1905, when fishing pressure had increased markedly, the Georgian Bay Fisheries Commission stated that a gang consisted of 18 to 20 boxes, each box containing three pieces, or individual nets, each of which was 250 yards long and about 2 yards deep. The gang would be about 14 000 yards long by perhaps 2 yards deep.[15]

The Indians used gill nets, as well as seines, in the pre-contact period. In the commercial fishery, gill nets were in use in the deeper waters off Prince Edward County as early as 1840 and are still the most common gear used there.[16] In Lake Huron they were probably in use from the inception of American fishery in such places as Mackinac. Gill nets were in use at Southampton at the base of the Bruce Peninsula from about 1855 and in Georgian Bay from 1835 or 1838.[17] On Lake Superior the American Fur Company used gill nets from the beginning of its fishing operations.[18] On Lake Erie gill nets were in use by the 1870s, but pound nets remained the dominant gear into the twentieth century.[19]

By the early 1870s gill nets and pound nets had replaced seines as the principal fishing gear except in specialized fisheries such as those on the St. Clair–Detroit River system and in enclosed waters such as Rondeau Harbour, Long Point Bay in Lake Erie, Burlington Bay, and Toronto Harbour. Specialized fisheries, particularly those in the Bay of Quinte, also made, and still make, use of nets such as the hoop, or fyke, net. Hoop nets are small-scale variations of pound nets in which fish are led into a series of enclosed spaces from which it is unlikely they can escape.

Gill nets were generally cheaper to operate than pound nets both in terms of capital expenses and labour. In 1890 a pound net and boat could be purchased for $1000 while a gang of gill nets and boat cost $500. The relative investment in the two types of fishery has remained constant over the years: a 1953 study found the average gill-net operator's investment to be $50 000 and the average pound-net operator's investment about $100 000. If necessary, gill nets could be operated by one man. Pound nets required several men to operate and were usually not profitable unless a fisherman had two or three nets so that his men would be fully employed.[20] Consequently the ownership of pound nets was restricted to fishermen with some capital. Gill nets could be used virtually as long as the lakes were open although the risk of loss of nets, or of life, certainly increased in the winter. Pound nets were more susceptible to storm and ice damage than were gill nets and usually were taken out of the water before the winter storms. Gill nets were much more flexible than pound nets and could be easily moved to new locations; in particular they could be used in deep waters that had not, at the time of their introduction, been overfished. The major disadvantage of gill nets was that fish caught in them died within a few hours or days, and if the net could not be lifted for several days, whether because of bad weather or other reasons, many of the fish spoiled. Pound-net fishermen alleged that gill-net fishermen regularly fished more net than they could properly handle, with the result that many fish were wasted. As well, gill nets were often lost and drifted about for weeks or months catching fish. The decaying fish were wasted and constituted a form of pollution that, it was believed, drove other fish away from the fishing grounds. Pound nets kept fish alive and in prime condition until they were taken from the water; fish buyers preferred fish from pound nets and were sometimes willing to pay a premium for them.[21]

Towards the end of the nineteenth century a variation on the pound net, the trap net, was introduced on the Great Lakes. It was similar in design to a pound net except that it was maintained in position by anchors and floats rather than by stakes. The pot, which was under water, was completely enclosed. It could be used in water where a staked net was not practical and could be moved more easily than a staked net. Trap nets were popular in American waters but were not permitted in Canadian waters. Because they were very efficient at catching fish, many fishermen feared they would result in overfishing, and they were opposed as a conservation measure. Although illegal, they were widely used in Georgian Bay at the turn of the century. When they were discovered they were destroyed. Trap nets were finally made legal in Canada in 1950 and have completely replaced pound nets.[22]

About 1905, American fishermen on Lake Erie developed a variation on the gill net, the bull net. A bull net was simply a very deep gill net. At the time a typical "narrow" net (used for herring and other small fish) was 22 mesh or about 5 feet deep; bull nets were up to 100 mesh or 22 feet deep. These nets were much more efficient than standard gill nets; in fact, they were so efficient that by 1934 most jurisdictions had outlawed them.[23] To what extent they were adopted in Canada is not known although they were used at Port Dover in the early 1920s. Port Dover fishermen protested vigorously against a move to ban them in 1922, and bull nets remained legal in the Ontario waters of Lake Erie as long as they were legal in any one of the states that bordered on Lake Erie.[24] Another variation in the use of gill

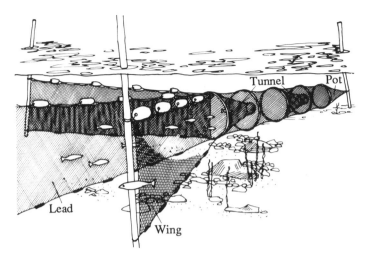
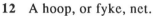

12 A hoop, or fyke, net.

G.F. Adams and D.P. Kolenosky, *Out of the Water: Ontario's Freshwater Fish Industry* ([Toronto]: Commercial Fish and Fur Branch, Ontario Ministry of Natural Resources, 1974), p. 11.

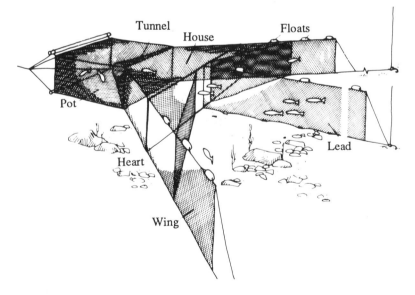

13 A trap net.

G.F. Adams and D.P. Kolenosky, *Out of the Water: Ontario's Freshwater Fish Industry* ([Toronto]: Commercial Fish and Fur Branch, Ontario Ministry of Natural Resources, 1974), p. 11.

nets, canning, was introduced about 1900. Traditionally gill nets had rested on the bottom of the lake, but it was found that by canning, floating the nets at varying depths according to season and water temperature, the catch could be increased.[25]

Originally all nets were hand-made, often by fishermen's wives, but after the 1840s machine-made nets were imported from Scotland and gradually replaced hand-made nets. Most of the nets used in the early fishery were made of linen. About 1900, cotton nets were introduced and, largely because they were cheaper, they generally replaced linen nets except on Lake Ontario where many fishermen continued to use linen gill nets for whitefish until 1950.[26] About 1950, cotton and linen gill nets were almost completely displaced by nylon nets, and within a decade the remaining pound and trap nets were also made of nylon.[27] Because nylon nets did not absorb water they were lighter and easier to handle than cotton nets. They were also more resistant to decay than natural-fibre nets, which had to be treated regularly. Pound nets were tarred at the beginning of the season and again about midsummer. Gill nets were treated by being soaked in preservatives such as kerosene, bluestone, or slaked lime; in addition they were regularly brought ashore to be dried and mended. In some cases, particularly when the water was warm, all of the nets that were lifted each day would be brought ashore to dry; when the water was colder all, or a portion, of the nets might be reset without being dried on shore. In general, nylon nets could be left in the water longer and required less handling. Most important, because they were almost invisible to fish, they were up to three times as efficient as the natural-fibre nets.[28] The introduction of nylon nets may have been the cause of the small and short-lived revival of the whitefish fishery in Lakes Erie and Huron in the late 1940s and early 1950s.

The first nets used wooden floats, soaked in linseed oil, and stones for sinkers. The floats were called corks even though they were usually made of cedar, which did not become waterlogged as easily as cork. About the time of World War II, plastic or aluminum floats replaced wood; lead weights had replaced stone during the nineteenth century.[29]

The most recent innovation in fishing nets is the trawl. Essentially a trawl is a large net bag that is towed through the water slightly above, or on, the lake bed by a boat. On modern boats sophisticated electronic gear is used to locate schools of fish. The fish are swept up by the net as it is towed along and when it is judged to be full the net is hauled to the boat, hoisted on board, and emptied. Trawls were in use in the nineteenth century in sea fisheries, but they were not introduced in the Great Lakes until the late 1950s when the abundance of smelt in Lake Erie made them practical. Smelt

14 Nets drying at Port Dover, 1915.
Photo by John Boyd. National Archives of Canada, PA 71643.

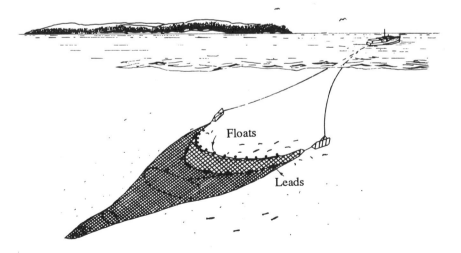

Floats

Leads

15 A trawl.
G.F. Adams and D.P. Kolenosky, *Out of the Water: Ontario's Freshwater Fish Industry* ([Toronto]:
Commercial Fish and Fur Branch, Ontario Ministry of Natural Resources, 1974), p. 13.

16 Raising the trawl on a Lake Erie tug.
Communications Directorate, Department of Fisheries and Oceans, Ottawa.

had been plentiful in Lake Erie for at least a decade before they were caught commercially in large numbers. They were not valuable enough to be picked by hand from gill nets except in Lake Ontario, where they were unusually large. Some were caught in small-mesh pound nets or in trap nets, but these were only effective in spring. Trawls were effective in all seasons and did not require hand picking. In addition, trawlers could be operated by two or three men whereas even a small gill-net tug had a crew of four.[30] Trawls are best suited to shallow to intermediate water depths where the bottom is smooth and free from snags. Today, although most trawls are used on Lake Erie, they have been used on the other Great Lakes. On Lake Superior, trawls have been used to catch herring. Although they could be used to catch more valuable fish than smelt, such use is not permitted.

Technological Development: Boats

The latter half of the nineteenth century witnessed a major change in the types of boats used in the Great Lakes fishery. The seine, spear, and hook fisheries required little more than small rowboats or canoes, but pound fisheries required more specialized boats. Pound-net boats had to be broad enough to provide stable platforms for lifting the nets. They also had to have large carrying capacities as well as shallow drafts so that they could enter pots to empty nets. The shallow draft and flat bottom were also assets for boats that operated from beaches rather than proper harbours. In 1880 an American observer described the pound-net boats in western Lake Erie as being large, many of them 30 feet long and 10 feet wide, with burthens of from 7 to 10 tons. Each had a centreboard, two masts from 35 to 40 feet long, and a gaff topsail.[1] Shortly after 1900, gasoline engines were introduced in pound boats and quickly became popular.[2] A notable feature of the powered pound-net boat was a hinged propellor shaft that allowed the propellor to be raised when the boat entered the pot.

In addition to the pound boat, a pound-net operation required a scow equipped with a pile driver for driving stakes and with tackle for lifting them. Early scows were sailed or rowed; later scows were towed into position by powered boats. Originally the pile driver was operated by hand, and not surprisingly, the setting of the nets was considered the heaviest labour of the fishing season. In later years pile drivers were operated by steam or gas engines.[3]

On Lake Huron and Lake Superior, where pound nets were less common than gill nets and where there were more good harbours, boats adapted to deepwater fishing were developed. There were two main recognizable

17 A Cleveland pound-net boat, ca. 1885. The Cleveland was one of many variations of the pound-net boat.

H.M. Smith and M.-M. Snell, comp., "Fisheries of the Great Lakes in 1885...," in U.S. Commission of Fish and Fisheries, *Report of the Commissioner for 1887*, USGPO, Washington, D.C., 1891, App. 1, Pl. 7.

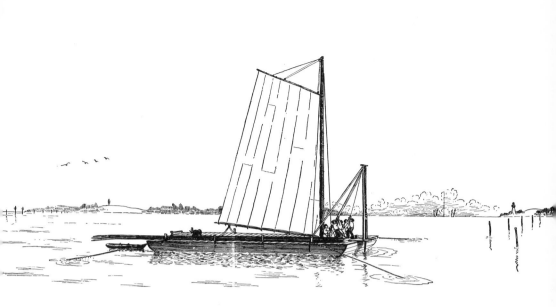

18 Stake boat, ca. 1885.

H.M. Smith and M.-M. Snell, comp., "Fisheries of the Great Lakes in 1885...," in U.S. Commission of Fish and Fisheries, *Report of the Commissioner for 1887*, USGPO, Washington, D.C., 1891, App. 1, Pl. 9.

19 Stake boat, pre-1925, with a steam-powered pile driver.

W.N. Koelz, "Fishing Industry of the Great Lakes," in U.S. Bureau of Fisheries, *Report of the United States Commissioner of Fisheries ... 1925*, USGPO, Washington, D.C., 1926, App. 11, Fig. 13.

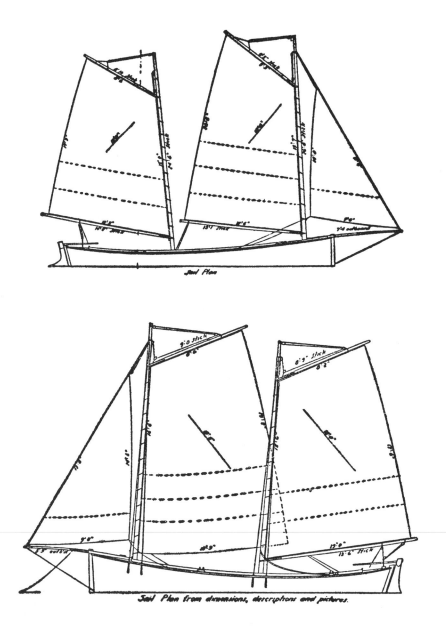

20 Lake Huron Mackinaw boat or "Collingwood skiff" (*top*) and a
Mackinaw boat for the western lakes (*bottom*).

Howard I. Chapelle, *American Small Sailing Craft, Their Design, Development,
and Construction* (New York: W.W. Norton & Co., 1951), pp. 181, 183.
Reproduced by permission of W.W. Norton & Company, Inc.

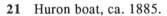

21 Huron boat, ca. 1885.

H.M. Smith and M.-M. Snell, comp., "Fisheries of the Great Lakes in 1885...," in U.S. Commission of Fish and Fisheries, *Report of the Commissioner for 1887*, USGPO, Washington, D.C., 1891, App. 1, Pl. 4.

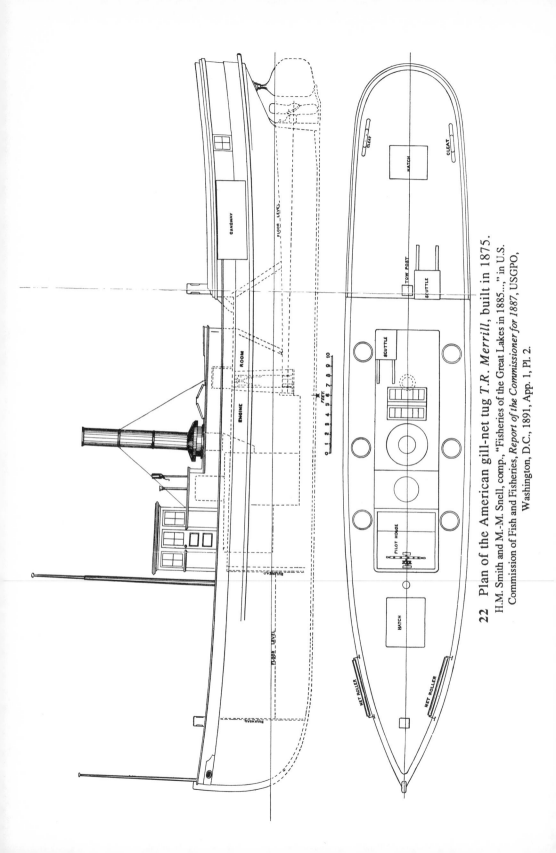

22 Plan of the American gill-net tug *T.R. Merrill*, built in 1875.
H.M. Smith and M.-M. Snell, comp., "Fisheries of the Great Lakes in 1885...," in U.S.
Commission of Fish and Fisheries, *Report of the Commissioner for 1887*, USGPO,
Washington, D.C., 1891, App. 1, Pl. 2.

23 Fish tugs *Annie M.* and *Leighton McCarthy* at Collingwood, 1915.
National Archives of Canada, PA 71649.

types: the Mackinaw and the Huron boat. In Georgian Bay the Mackinaw boat was often called a Collingwood boat and may have originated at Collingwood in the 1850s. It was a double-ended boat, open except for a small foredeck, and was usually under 30 feet in length. An example described in 1885 was 28 feet in length and 7 feet 6 inches in beam, and drew 22 inches of water with its centreboard up. Its two masts were 28 feet long and its bowsprit was 6 feet.[4] It carried a jib, a loose-footed gaff foresail, and a boom-and-gaff mainsail. The Mackinaw had the reputation of being remarkably seaworthy, but was short of cargo space and was only used with light (small) rigs of gill nets. It was used in Georgian Bay, the North Channel of Lake Huron, and in Lake Superior. The Huron boat was a larger, square-sterned, two-masted boat with a heart-shaped transom. It was from 30 to 40 feet long and 8 or 9 feet wide and had more cargo-carrying room than the Mackinaw boat. Huron boats usually fished heavy rigs in deep water and went farther from shore than the Mackinaws. They were most common on Lake Huron proper and on Lake Michigan.[5] In the mid-1870s, steam-powered fishing boats were introduced on the lakes. The early boats were modelled on steam tugs and were sometimes used for towing in the off season; as a result they were, and are, known as fishing tugs.[6] The first steam-powered boats, although not large, were bigger than the sailboats. A typical tug might have been 50 feet long and 12 to 14 feet wide. They were heavily built of wood with a heavy deck and substantial freeboard. The steam engine, boilers, and coal bunkers were amidships, fish storage was below the foredeck, and net storage was below the afterdeck. The afterdeck was sometimes raised to increase storage room. Storage was a problem, and nets and fish were often stored on deck, with the result that the boats were unstable. The earliest tugs had foremasts to provide sailpower in emergencies, and foremasts also served as derricks for handling nets and fish. Typically a tug's crew consisted of a captain, an engineer, and five fishermen.[7] Tugs were used principally in the gill-net fishery but were also used as auxiliaries in the pound fishery, where they offloaded fish from pound-net boats, towed pound boats from pound to pound, and carried fish to markets. The tugs increased the intensity of fishing on all the lakes.

Because of their size tugs could fish in worse weather and farther from shore than most sailboats. Because of their speed they spent less time travelling and more time lifting nets; consequently they could fish more nets per man than could the sailboats. One estimate was that three men using sails or oars could handle 6000 yards of gill net or two pound nets; six men with a tug could handle 60 000 yards of gill net or ten pounds.[8] This advantage was increased after 1900 when powered net-lifters were developed[9] and speeded up the laborious and time-consuming task of lifting nets. One fisherman estimated that they doubled the amount of net that could be handled.[10]

Tugs did not become numerous until the 1890s. In 1895 there were 11 on the Canadian side of Lake Superior, 43 on Lake Huron, 19 on Lake Erie, and 4 on Lake Ontario. The use of steam tugs peaked about the end of the First World War: in 1919 there were 119 tugs with average burthens of 25 tons on the lakes. Some much larger tugs, such as the *Earl Bess*, 118 tons and 81 feet in length, were built during the prosperous decade 1910–20. Such large tugs were exceptional and by the late 1920s, steam tugs were beginning to be replaced by smaller diesel- or gasoline-powered tugs that were cheaper to operate.[11]

Perhaps because of the popular interest in steam power and because of the association of steam tugs with what is considered the heyday of the fishery, the image of the steam tug has come to dominate the image of the fishery in the early years of the century. This image should be tempered by the knowledge that smaller boats remained a very important part of the industry. In 1919 when there were 119 tugs employing 706 men on the Great

Lakes, there were also 626 gasoline launches that employed 1361 men and 984 sail- and rowboats that employed 1475 men.

The first diesel-powered boat on the north shore of Lake Erie was built in 1920, and during the 1920s and 1930s the fleets on the Great Lakes were gradually converted to diesel power.[12] Diesel engines and their fuel were less bulky than steam engines and their fuel; consequently conversion to diesel power increased working and storage space on the boats. Diesel engines did not require an engineer; consequently crew size and operating costs were reduced. At the same time as the fleets were converted to diesel power, the first steel-hulled boats were built and they gradually replaced wooden hulls.[13]

Superstructures were also changed gradually. The original tugs had been open except for wheelhouses and engine rooms. Late in the nineteenth century the afterdeck, where fish were picked from the nets, was lightly enclosed with awnings and canvas side curtains. Then the foredeck was partially and eventually completely enclosed, and the afterdeck was more substantially enclosed. The distinctive rounded form of the bow enclosure gave rise to the description "turtle deck" (see Fig. 24). By World War II the large gill-net boat looked much as it does today with a high boxlike superstructure extending from bow to stern. Both the lifting and setting of nets is accomplished through large sliding doors. As the superstructure was enclosed, the need for the heavy main deck was reduced and storage space low in the hull was increased. The change from steam to diesel power also increased storage space in the hull, with the result that the boat's centre of gravity was lowered in spite of the high profile that the superstructure gave it.[14]

The introduction of trawling in the 1960s required modifications in the standard gill-net tug; however, since many boats continued to fish gill nets as well as trawls, the basic features of the gill-net tug were retained. A winch, usually powered by an old automobile engine, was installed on the afterdeck to raise the heavy trawl. A towing frame was welded on the superstructure, and a vertical A frame was added to help lift the trawl from the water. The stern doors had to be enlarged to handle trawls.[15] Almost all of the boats have been, and are, locally built on Lake Erie and in Georgian Bay, and in some cases boats are still built by the fishermen themselves.[16]

24 The *Charles P. Stricker* has a partial turtle deck; the *Atlas* is fully enclosed forward. Ca. 1910.

W.N. Koelz, "Fishing Industry of the Great Lakes," in U.S. Bureau of Fisheries, *Report of the United States Commissioner of Fisheries ... 1925*, USGPO, Washington, D.C., 1926, App. 11, Fig. 3.

25 The *Dover Rose*, a Lake Erie trawler.

Communications Directorate, Department of Fisheries and Oceans, Ottawa.

Technological Development
Processing and Distribution

Prior to the 1860s almost all fish were either sold fresh and in the round (whole) or were salted. In general, fresh fish were only available in local markets because transportation was not rapid enough to move them to distant markets. Fish that were not sold fresh were cleaned (with the backbone left in), beheaded, and packed in barrels of brine. Well-packed fish would keep for months. Many of the salted fish were sold locally as winter provisions, but salt fish were also shipped to distant markets. John Askin shipped salt fish from Sault Ste. Marie to Detroit in 1809, and Ohio fishermen began to ship salted whitefish to New York shortly after the Erie Canal opened in 1825.[1] The American Fur Company shipped most of its Lake Superior fish to Michigan and Ohio markets, but some were shipped as far as New York and the southern United States.[2]

Where adequate transportation existed, fish were exported fresh on ice. On Lakes Huron and Superior they were packed in large insulated carts that held as much as a ton of fish; on Lake Erie much smaller 100- and 200-pound boxes were used.[3] Fresh iced fish were shipped from Goderich and Collingwood to Toronto by rail in 1856.[4] Shipments of fresh fish from upper Lake Huron and Superior gradually increased, but it was not until the early 1880s that icehouses became common on upper Georgian Bay and shipments of fresh fish from Lake Superior and Manitoulin Island exceeded shipments of salt fish. By the turn of the century, salt fish were uncommon except for herring, which were salted as a specialty item.[5]

Freezing, as opposed to placing fresh fish on ice, was introduced at Camden, Maine, in 1861, and in 1869 and 1875 W. and S.H. Davis of Detroit patented a system in which fish were placed in covered metal trays that were

26 A wheeled shipping box or cart used on the upper lakes.

Charles W. Triggs, "The Problem of Getting our Fish to the Customer. Distribution," *Fishing Gazette*, Vol. 52, No. 7, Annual Review Number (1935), p. 103.

27 Bagging herring that have been frozen in the open air at Port Arthur, ca. 1930.

"The Inland Fisheries," *Canadian Fisheries Manual* (1932), p. 69.

packed in ice and salt and then frozen.[6] The system was in use in major American Great Lakes shipping centres in the early 1870s. By 1885 Sandusky, Ohio, the major fish-packing centre on the lakes, froze 3.3 million pounds of fish annually compared to 9 million pounds sold fresh, 5.9 million pounds salted, and 2.3 million pounds smoked.[7] Fresh fish preserved on ice remained the most common form marketed until well into the twentieth century, but freezing played an important role in levelling supply and demand conditions. Fish supply was prone to gluts and shortages, and freezing allowed fish to be held over until periods of scarcity. Demand was also uneven; much of the catch from Lake Erie and Lake Ontario went to supply the Jewish market in New York and demand peaked during Jewish holy days. Fishermen who had freezing equipment could gain some control over marketing and prices.

Information on the introduction of freezers into Ontario is sketchy. One of the earliest freezers was built at Southampton in 1879, and there were freezers at Wiarton, Collingwood, Meaford, and the Duck Islands on Lake Huron by 1890.[8] On Lake Erie, where a large proportion of Canadian fish were shipped directly to American markets as soon as they were taken from the nets, freezers were less necessary; however, as the Canadian fishery became increasingly independent in the 1930s, freezers became more common.[9]

The principal drawback of the salt and ice method of freezing was that it was slow. As a result, expanding ice crystals destroyed the fish's cell structure and when the fish was thawed it was soft and watery. In 1892 a second method of freezing, using refrigerated ammonia, was introduced at Sandusky, and after World War I, freezing using chilled brine became common.[10] Two of the most successful brine systems (using a calcium chloride solution) were developed by the Kolbe family at Port Dover in 1925 and 1927. In the Kolbe "diving bell" system, fish were placed in shallow covered pans. The pans were then placed in a rack and lowered into a tank of chilled brine. In the "floating pan" method, fish were placed in circular pans and floated in chilled brine.[11]

The "floating pan" system was particularly well-adapted to freezing fillets. Filleting was introduced in North America early in the twentieth century but did not become common on the Great Lakes until the late 1920s.[12] Prior to the 1930s most fish, particularly if they were destined for the New York market, were shipped in the round. Fish destined for Chicago were more likely to be dressed (beheaded and eviscerated). Filleting reduced the weight of fish handled and consequently reduced freezing time and shipping charges.

Fillets were an early example of convenience foods. A more recent example, fish sticks, allows the industry to make use of coarse fish that are still abundant in the lakes. Fish sticks were first produced in the United States in 1952–53 and in Ontario in 1954.[13] Even more recently, the development of a mechanized means of cleaning smelt has been crucial to the industry. The small size and low unit value of smelt made them uneconomic to clean by hand. In the early 1960s the Omstead Fishery (now Omstead Foods) of Wheatley, Ontario, developed a machine for processing smelt. Omstead's ability to process large quantities of smelt at a relatively low cost was an important factor in its emergence as the major fishing company on the Canadian side of the lakes in the 1960s.[14]

Improvements in the means of handling and processing fish developed in tandem with improved means of distributing them to a wider market. Originally, fresh fish had only been available in local markets, and salt fish were shipped by sailboat and canal barge to distant markets. The introduction of steam navigation combined with the use of ice made it possible for fresh fish to be shipped to the larger American markets. Fish from Lakes Superior and Huron and the Detroit River system were shipped to Detroit or Chicago; fish from the east end of Lake Ontario were shipped to Oswego, Cape Vincent, and Sackets Harbor in New York; and fish from Lake Erie were shipped to the American Lake Erie ports of Buffalo, Erie, Sandusky, Cleveland, and Detroit.

American packing companies operated steamers that visited Canadian fishing stations on a regular basis and took their catch to the United States. On the western end of Lake Erie, fish caught in Canadian waters were not even landed in Canada but were transferred directly from Canadian fishing boats to the American steamers. From American ports the fish were sent by rail to the principal American fish markets, New York and Chicago. As the Canadian railway system developed it provided alternatives to shipment by water. Fish from Goderich, Point Edward, Cape Rich, and Collingwood were being shipped by rail as early as 1859, and the construction of the Canadian Pacific Railway in 1885 opened up markets for fish from Lake Superior. On Lake Erie, fish from most major ports could be shipped by rail by the 1890s, but the convenience of shipping by boat to the ports on the opposite side of the lake kept some boats in business until after the First World War. Railways, however, were able to give faster, direct service to the principal markets in New York and Chicago and they superseded boats. In the 1930s, fishermen began shipping by truck, and refrigerated trucks now handle almost all Great Lakes fish.[15]

28 Dock at Jackfish, Lake Superior, ca. 1930. The construction of the CPR opened new markets for fish from Lake Superior.

National Archives of Canada, PA 32450.

Ownership and Marketing

The principal trends in ownership of the Great Lakes fishing operations during the nineteenth century were growth in scale of individual firms, corporate control of the entire fishery, and increasing American influence. In the first half of the nineteenth century, conditions on the lower lakes favoured small, independent fishermen. Prior to 1857 there was no legal restriction on entering the fishery; after 1857, licences were required but fees were low and before the 1890s there were no limitations on the number of licences issued. The capital required for a seine- or a gill-net fishery was small, and sites were readily available. On Lake Ontario, sites at Burlington Beach and in Prince Edward County were acquired on the basis of squatter's rights and the "owners" vigorously resisted the government's attempts to collect licence fees after 1857.[1] A similar situation seems to have existed on Lake Erie, where the best seining sites were occupied by squatters; Thomas Paxton, who had obtained a licence to occupy Point Pelee in 1846, could not operate his fishery there because the lease was occupied by ten families of squatters.[2]

Labour costs were also low. Gill-net fisheries could be operated single handed or with two or three men; seine fisheries usually employed a gang of about five men. In many cases fisheries could have been operated as family enterprises or as partnerships with no outlay for wages. Partnerships may have been common on Lakes Huron and Superior, where the fishery overseer reported that in 1859 he had issued 97 leases on the two lakes; 12 were to Indian bands and 14 were to the Hudson's Bay Company.[3] Most of the rest were to groups of fishermen or merchants who were evidently in partnerships. Where labour was hired, actual outlay was kept low by fishing on shares.[4] Marketing costs for fish on the lower lakes were also low.

Most of the fish were sold fresh in local markets, and it is probable that most were sold direct to the consumer for cash or were bartered.

Although conditions on the lower lakes favoured small fisheries, there were larger fisheries operated by small capitalists. In 1827 Thomas Paxton obtained a licence of occupation for Fighting (Turkey) Island in the Detroit River and operated a fishery there for the next 50 years. His fishery was one of the largest in the area; in 1856 he packed 2500 barrels of whitefish.[5] It was evidently operated with hired labour paid monthly wages. Several other fisheries were established on the basis of licences of occupation: Alexander McGregor's at the Fishing Islands in 1832; the Huron Fishing Company's, also at the Fishing Islands, in 1834; and John Prince's at Rondeau in 1848.[6] Little is known of how these fisheries were operated. Prince and the organizers of the Huron Fishing Company were developers and would not have engaged personally in the fishery; McGregor was involved in fisheries all his life and may have operated his fishery personally. There was also at least one large fishing firm on Lake Ontario; a Mr. Geddes leased the fisheries on the west side of Toronto Island in 1846 and employed 30 to 40 men.[7]

Very little is known of the earliest fisheries on northern Lake Huron, but the reports of the fishery overseers in the late 1850s indicate that many of the fisheries were operated by individuals, in many cases Indians, who sold their catch to American merchants who cruised the area. Often the merchants advanced the nets used and received their payment in fish.[8]

On Lake Superior the fishery was developed and dominated by two large and well-capitalized corporations, the American Fur Company and the Hudson's Bay Company. Both companies had the capital necessary to establish large-scale operations in a remote area and to build the boats required to transport fish to outside markets. In addition they had the capital to await results and suffer some losses. Their salt fish were not sold for ready cash but were shipped to forwarders on the lower lakes on consignment, and the forwarders sent them on to market in New York or the midwest and south. The companies had to wait months for payments and suffered losses due to spoilage, market fluctuations, and misadventure.[9] The American Fur Company failed in 1842, but the Hudson's Bay Company remained the dominant fishing operation on the Canadian waters of Lake Superior until the late 1850s, when the development of public steam transportation opened the lake to smaller operations.

The two companies also had an advantage in the sparsely populated Lake Superior region in that they had management and labour in the area. In fact, one incentive for the companies to develop commercial fishing was that it employed surplus labour.

Technological changes in the last half of the nineteenth century increased the cost of fishing operations, reduced the role of the small independent fisherman, and led to a concentration of control, if not ownership, of the fishery in a few hands. Early seines were worth, at most, a few hundred dollars, and a small gill-net operation using a sailboat could be established for $500. Pound nets, tugs, icehouses, and refrigeration units all increased capital requirements. By 1893 a successful Lake Erie pound-net operation might include a tug worth $3000, ten pound nets worth $300 each, an icehouse and freezer worth $1000, and net boats, stake scows, and pile drivers worth $700. It would employ at least six men at annual wages of about $350 each.[10]

Much larger fisheries existed. C.W. Gauthier of Windsor, one of the leading fishermen on the Canadian lakes, reported in 1884 that he employed 200 men and a capital of $200 000 (he may have included his operations in Manitoba in these figures).[11] Eight years later his principal rival on Lake Huron, J. Clarke of the Buffalo Fish Company, reported that his firm owned 13 tugs and bought fish from many more.[12] At the time there were only 67 licensed tugs on the lakes; how many Gauthier controlled is not known, but two smaller companies owned 4 each, two owned 3 each, and at least five owned 2 each.[13]

Small companies and individual firms continued to operate, but they were overshadowed by the larger companies and their independence was limited. The small companies were increasingly confined to the primary fishery, the catching of the fish. The larger companies bought fish directly from the fishermen's boats, packed them, shipped them, and to some extent handled the marketing. Packing, shipping, and marketing were often more lucrative than the actual fishing and allowed dealers to accumulate capital and enlarge their operations. Although the history of the fish-buying firms is vague, it is known that by the late 1880s a number of medium and large firms had established areas of influence. For example, C.W. Gauthier centred his operations on the Duck Islands in Lake Huron, J. Clarke of Goderich had a depot on Squaw Island in Georgian Bay, Noble Brothers operated in the vicinity of Killarney, Booth Fisheries had a base at Quebec Harbour, Michipicoten Island, on Lake Superior, J.W. Post of Sandusky traded in the western end of Lake Erie, and the Buffalo Fish Company traded in the eastern end of Lake Erie and on Lake Huron.

In addition to operating fishing fleets, the firms bought from other fishermen in their own areas. These fishermen were nominally independent but were often indebted to the larger firms. For example, J.W. Post operated two steamers that made daily trips from Rondeau west along the Lake Erie

29 Killarney harbour, probably late nineteenth century. Most of the boats appear to be Mackinaws but one in the left background has the heart-shaped transom of a Huron boat.

Photo by W.J. Topley. National Archives of Canada, PA 8555.

shore; his agents bought fish from pound nets and sold them to wholesalers in Sandusky. When Post testified before the Dominion Fishery Commission (1894) he stated that he bought all of the fish from 22 nets in the region and had bought from as many as 32. Although he had "started" all of the fishermen whose catches he bought and still held mortgages on their boats, he considered them to be independent.[14] This independence was questioned in the testimony of William Haskins, who had held a fishing station in the 1880s. Post held a mortgage on the station and in 1885 forced Haskins to sell to him. In spite of the sale, the licence continued to be issued in Haskin's name; Post, as an American, could not have held it in his own name. J.W. Kerr, the fishery overseer in the region, believed that Post owned most of the nets from which he bought fish and that he used his influence with a local fishery officer to deny licences to fishermen who refused to sell their fish to him.[15]

James Clarke, a representative of the Buffalo Fish Company on Lake Huron, testified that although he fished two nets in his own name, he was "interested" in more or less all of the nets from which he bought fish, and that the company (in which he owned shares) supplied its fishermen with nets.[16] In some cases firms such as Noble Brothers applied for licences in the names of their fishermen, advanced the fishermen the money for the licences, and kept the licences when they were issued.[17] These practices all kept nominally independent fishermen dependent on the larger companies.

At the same time as control of the fishery was concentrated in the hands of the larger companies, the larger companies came under American control. Americans had always been involved in the fishery. Fishery officers appointed in 1857 found that in many cases, especially on Lake Erie and the northern shores of Lake Huron, Americans had been fishing in Canadian waters and exporting the fish.[18] The officers were able to stop most American fishing in Canadian waters except for sporadic poaching, but they were unable to affect American control of the fishery exercised through American control of the market.

American influence grew as the proportion of the catch that was exported to the United States grew. The growth of the export market is difficult to document because no reliable figures as to the size of the export trade are available for the nineteenth and early twentieth centuries. No record was kept of fish exported from Canada. In many cases they were not even landed in Canada but were taken directly from the nets to U.S ports. On the other hand, relatively few fish appear in American records as having been imported from Canada; if they were caught in American-owned nets they would be treated as American fish and no duty paid. Consequently import-export records are non-existent or unreliable. In general all statistics relating to sales and catch for both American and Canadian waters, including those in Tables 1 and 2, must be considered approximations.

It is known that fish from the eastern end of Lake Ontario, the western end of Lake Erie, and Lake Huron were being exported in the 1850s and earlier, but as late as 1871, reports indicate that most fish were shipped to Canadian markets.[19] The export trade grew rapidly and by 1900 it was commonly estimated that over 90 per cent of the Canadian catch was exported to the United States. There even were complaints that it was difficult to buy Ontario fish in local markets.[20] Such complaints continued up to the time of World War I, and in 1918 the Ontario government established a Fish Sales Branch with power to purchase up to 20 per cent of the total catch at fixed prices and to arrange for its distribution and sale on domestic markets.

Under the program, discontinued in 1922, about ten million pounds of fish were purchased.[21]

American control of the Canadian fishery was strengthened by changes in the tariff structure. Prior to 1890, Canadian fish were exported to the United States duty free, but beginning in October 1890 a tariff of three-quarters of a cent per pound was put on both fresh and frozen fish. For many low-priced fish the tariff would have been prohibitive, but American customs officials took the view that fish caught by Americans or in nets owned by Americans were American even if they came from Canadian waters.[22] Consequently American firms that had advanced materials or money for nets used by Canadian fishermen could declare that they owned the nets and have fish caught in those nets admitted duty free. Canadian fishermen who attempted to export fish had to pay the duty. As a result many Canadian fishermen were forced into alliances with American firms or became bound to them by debt.

To escape the duty two major Canadian dealers, C.W. Gauthier of Windsor and J. Clarke of Collingwood, transferred their operations to the United States. Clarke became an agent of the Buffalo Fish Company; he was a shareholder as well and may have been the controlling shareholder. C.W. Gauthier became involved with both the Detroit Fish Company and the Manitoba Fish Company. His exact relationship to either company is unclear although he was sometimes referred to as the manager of the Detroit Fish Company.[23]

On Lake Superior the A. Booth Packing Company was the dominant firm in the 1890s. It began as a small fish dealership in Chicago in 1848 and expanded gradually; its first known Canadian operations were on Lake Winnipeg in 1871. Because it was an American company it could not hold Canadian licences directly, but it used its market power to control fishermen and in many cases held licences through subsidiary companies. The Port Arthur Fish Company, which had packing plants at Port Arthur and Rossport, was its agent on the western end of Lake Superior. In 1898 the company was reorganized and incorporated as A. Booth and Company, and at the same time the new corporation absorbed as many as 43 other fishing companies. By one report the Booth trust controlled 80 per cent of freshwater fish dealers and 150 million pounds of fish annually. Although all of the companies that were involved in the trust are not known, they included, or were soon to include, the Port Arthur Fish Company, the Buffalo Fish Company, Ganly and Ainsworth of Sault Ste. Marie, Noble Brothers of Killarney, D. McLeod of Southampton, the Georgian Bay Fish Company of Collingwood, and M. Doyle of Toronto.[24] In 1899 the trust's Canadian holdings were absorbed into the Dominion Fish Company, a subsidiary of A. Booth and Company. Many of the Canadian dealers who had been absorbed by Booth continued to be associated with the Dominion Fish Company: James Clark of the Buffalo Fish Company was one of its organizers, and Noble Brothers and Ganly and Ainsworth acted as its local agents.[25]

In addition to gaining almost complete control of the fishery on the upper lakes and Lake Ontario, Booth also controlled the inland fisheries in western Canada and had extensive interests in Atlantic and Pacific fisheries. Although Booth purchased fish on Lake Erie, the company did not dominate the fishery there, possibly because the Erie fishery had direct access to New York markets. The company failed in 1909 but was reorganized and continued to be a major force on the upper lakes until the 1930s. In 1932 the company failed again and in its subsequent reorganization it divested itself of most of its assets on the Great Lakes including the Dominion Fish Company, which was dissolved.[26] Booth Fisheries Corporation is now a subsidiary of Consolidated Foods of Chicago.

Ostensibly the Booth fish trust had been organized to steady the fish trade and eliminate the cutthroat competition that made it impossible for dealers to refuse undersize fish. These were both laudable goals, but Canadian fishermen complained that the elimination of competition had lowered the prices that they received and creamed off profits that legitimately belonged to Canadian fisheries. Canadian officials accused the trust of encouraging the flouting of Canadian regulations and of being particularly rapacious in exploiting the fishery.[27] Perhaps what was resented most was that, because of the emphasis on export markets, it became difficult to purchase Great Lakes fish in Ontario.[28] This resentment was never effectively translated into action that seriously affected the trust. On at least two occasions fishery officers who were suspected of working with the trust were dismissed,[29] and the government's attitude to two firms, Noble Brothers of Killarney and the Port Arthur Fish Company, was coloured by the belief that they were agents for Booth. Ontario's establishment of the Fish Sales Branch in 1918 was a serious threat to the trust, and if it had been given marketing monopoly of Canadian Great Lakes fish (on the pattern of the modern Freshwater Fish Marketing Board), it would have broken the trust in Ontario. However, the sales branch was discontinued in 1922. Economic factors, not government action, eventually led to the trust's failure.

At almost the same time that the Booth trust was consolidating its hold on the upper Great Lakes fisheries, a number of developments, particularly on Lake Erie, led to conditions that eventually weakened corporate control of the industry and reduced American influences in it. Improved transportation gradually freed fishermen in isolated ports from dependence on transportation provided by dealers. On Lake Erie the growth of the railroad network allowed fishermen to deal directly with wholesalers in Detroit, Buffalo, and New York without the need for intermediaries. The introduction of telephone service along the north shore of Lake Erie about 1905 contributed to the weakening of buyers such as J.W. Post of Sandusky. Prior to 1905, fish had often been sold under year-long contracts; after 1905, fishermen on the western end of Lake Erie were able to communicate directly on a daily basis with Detroit wholesalers and arrange for the sale of their own fish, which could be shipped by rail rather than by Post's boats.[30] As his control over the market diminished, Post became vulnerable because he could not, as an American, hold licences directly, and about 1910 the fishermen whom he had formerly controlled combined and squeezed him out of the fishery.[31]

Other fishermen also banded together in small companies or co-operatives to resist the influence of the larger companies and to strengthen their bargaining positions. At Rossport on Lake Superior a group of fishermen co-operated to resist Booth's agent's attempts at monopoly control. The informal co-operative existed from about 1900 to about the end of World War I; it was gradually absorbed into the Nipigon Bay Fish Company.[32] At Port Stanley on Lake Erie the owners of 12 tugs organized the Producer's Fish Company in 1912. Its members bound themselves to sell all of their catch to the company, which sought to raise prices by limiting shipments and using freezers to avoid glutting the market during heavy runs. Although the company was successful initially, it went out of existence about 1918. The same group that organized the Producer's Fish Company also organized the Port Stanley Supply Company. The firm sold coal to the fishermen, but its principal operation was a fish-reduction plant that produced fish oil, fertilizer, and stock food from fish wastes. The company helped to reduce pollution from dumping fish wastes into the lake (a common but illegal practice) and provided a small market for otherwise unmarketable fish.[33]

Several other co-operative ventures were organized on Lake Erie during the 1920s, but all of them apparently failed prior to World War II. After the war there was a revival of interest in co-operative marketing and co-ops were organized at Port Dover, Port Maitland, Rondeau, Kingsville, and Port Rowan. These co-ops operated for about a decade and then began to fail as they had in the 1920s. An Ontario government investigation of Lake Erie fisheries in 1962 concluded that the co-ops were too loosely organized, members were not required to sell their fish to the co-ops, they were under-capitalized, and their management was weak.[34]

Trade associations were another form of co-operation. The first references to trade associations predate the First World War. In 1908 and 1913 the Protective Fisherman's Association and the Pond Net Fishermen's Association of South Essex lobbied the federal government for changes in fishery regulations.[35] The most powerful of the associations, the Lake Erie Fishermen's Association, was organized in 1916. In the same year a branch of the Canadian Fishermen's Association was organized on Lake Superior. In 1918 the Lake Huron and Georgian Bay Commercial Fishermen's Association was formed, and associations representing other lakes or areas were formed in subsequent years.[36]

The associations primarily acted as lobbies that attempted to influence fishing regulations and marketing conditions. The first major issue that the Lake Erie Fisherman's Association became involved in was the provincial government's wartime fish-purchasing policy. The Fish Sales Branch had the power to purchase, at a fixed rate, up to 20 per cent of each fisherman's catch, which it then sold to the public through retail fish dealers. The intent was to provide the public with fish, which otherwise would have been exported to the United States, at a low price and to free other food for the war effort. The fishermen argued that the policy failed to reduce costs to consumers at the same time as it reduced fishermen's returns below their production costs. Following vigorous protests from the fishermen and a change of government, the 20-per-cent quota was abandoned in 1920 and the entire policy of government purchasing of fish was abandoned in 1922.[37]

The Lake Erie Fisherman's Association's major emphasis was on securing favourable government regulations and support for the industry. During the 1920s it regularly passed resolutions calling for more effective patrols to prevent poaching by Americans, more emphasis on hatchery programs, and adjustments in regulations and fees that would allow Lake Erie fishermen to compete with American fishermen who, it was alleged, enjoyed much more liberal regulations than did Canadian fishermen.[38] The most contentious regulatory issue with which the association had to deal was the relationship between gill- and pound-net fishermen. There was a bitter debate as to the relative merits of pound and gill nets during the 1890s, and this led to attempts to have regulations favouring one type of net or the other.

On Lake Huron, where gillnetters were predominant, the pound net was banned from most of Georgian Bay in 1885, but on Lake Erie, pound-net fishermen were more powerful and initially were able to secure regulations that favoured them. From about 1915, gill-net fishermen were prevented from setting nets within ten miles of shore between Port Stanley and Point Pelee. On the rest of the lake, with the possible exception of the area off Long Point, they were required to set their nets at least five miles off shore so as not to interfere with the pound nets.[39] The gill-net fishermen argued that the regulation increased their travel time and costs, and in some seasons, reduced their catch. In spite of opposition from the gillnetters, the association endorsed the gill-net exclusion zone in 1921. At the same meeting it asked that gillnetters be required to fish out of their home ports and that the bull net, which was coming into use in the Port Dover area, be banned.[40] As a result, many gill-net fishermen left the association. Subsequently the association attempted to accommodate gillnetters and many returned to it in 1926.[41]

By the 1930s, gill-net fishermen had gained control of the association, and when it voted to eliminate the gill-net exclusion zone in 1931 and 1932,[42] pound-net fishermen left and formed their own organization that continued to lobby for the protection of pound-net fisheries.[43] Pound-net operators scored a victory in 1937 when the provincial government divided the lake into two districts along the extension of the Kent–Elgin County boundary line and prevented boats based on one side of the line from fishing on the other side.[44] Because most gill-net boats were based east of the line, the area west of the line was left to pound-net operators. The victory was a short-lived one, and early in the 1950s pound nets became uneconomic and were replaced by trap nets.

The Lake Erie Fishermen's Association, and other associations, also attempted to strengthen the fishermen's position vis-à-vis the fish buyers. Over much of the lakes in the years prior to 1900, fish were sold at fixed rates under annual contracts. By the 1890s, fishermen in the eastern half of Lake Erie had begun to send their fish directly to the Peck Slip Market, the major fish market in New York City. Fish were consigned to a particular Peck Slip merchant, who sold them at the market rate, took his commission (usually about 15 per cent) from the proceeds, and remitted the remainder to the shipper.[45]

The system was open to abuse and fishermen complained that they had not been paid, had not been paid in full, or had not received a fair price. At about the same time that the use of the telephone was introduced in the trade, the major Peck Slip merchants began to maintain purchasing agents in major fishing ports such as Port Dover. In ports where several competing agents were stationed, fishermen could play them off against one another; how-

30 Fish cleaners at a packing plant at Sandusky, Ohio, ca. 1885.
H.M. Smith and M.-M. Snell, comp., "Fisheries of the Great Lakes in 1885...," in U.S.
Commission of Fish and Fisheries, *Report of the Commissioner for 1887*, USGPO,
Washington, D.C., 1891, App. 1, Pl. 33.

ever, the advantage was limited, as agents knew the state of the market better than the fishermen did.[46]

In theory the agents bought the fish outright, thereby eliminating the problems of the consignment system, but they did not pay cash for fish and many of the alleged abuses of consignment dealing continued. On their side, the Peck Slip merchants argued that fluctuations in supply and market demand made it impossible to predict prices. More importantly, there was no control, either by the Canadian government or by the industry, of the quality of fish shipped from Canada. Quality varied and Peck Slip merchants often used poor quality as a justification for reducing prices specified on invoices.[47]

On at least two occasions the Lake Erie Fishermen's Association attempted to combat non-payment by establishing credit bureaus that circulated information on the reliability of the Peck Slip dealers; however, the attempts apparently failed for lack of support.[48] The association, or its leading members, also established co-operative marketing schemes in 1922, 1936, and in the late 1940s as means of coping with unscrupulous buyers. With the exception of the last attempt, the co-operative marketing schemes were all short-lived.[49]

The most effective response to the problems posed by the Peck Slip merchants and the fish trust came with the development of a number of relatively large integrated fisheries on the northern shore of Lake Erie. By 1919 there were approximately ten fisheries, employing from 10 to 30 men, that fished on their own account, bought fish from other fishermen, and packed and shipped fish. In the 1920s, when filleting fish became common, some of these medium-sized firms began to process fish as well. At the same time some of the companies began to use large freezing plants, which allowed them to regulate the amount of fish marketed and to take advantage of price fluctuations.

By controlling several steps in the marketing process, each of which held a possibility of profit, the companies were able to insulate their profits from the effects of changes in the price paid on Peck Slip. Packing was particularly important because packing charges were prorated in proportion to the market price of fish. If the catch declined and the market price per pound rose, then the price per pound for packing would also rise. Packers and processors who owned freezers charged for freezing; processors levied fixed charges for filleting or similar work. The various fixed charges that packers, shippers, and processors levied made their income more stable than that of fishermen, and they were able to accumulate capital and expand their businesses. Because they handled larger volumes of fish than any individual fisherman, they were able to bargain with the Peck Slip merchants on more equitable terms than most fishermen could. In fact, the packers and processors gradually replaced Peck Slip agents as the initial purchasers of fish on Lake Erie, and some fishermen believed that packers adopted the sharp practices of the Peck Slip merchants.[50]

One of the integrated firms that emerged during the 1920s was W.F. Kolbe and Company of Port Dover. William F. Kolbe began fishing in the United States in the 1870s and by 1911 was an established packer and shipper in Erie, Pennsylvania. In 1911 the firm opened a branch in Port Dover; subsequently it acquired packing depots at Erieau, Port Elgin, and Port Burwell, as well as two steamers, the *City of Dover* and the *Louise*. The steamers were used to deliver fish to American markets and to the Kolbe plant at Erie. In 1925 the firm built a 175-ton-capacity freezer plant at Port Dover. The plant used a brine freezing process that had been developed by Robert Kolbe and that was subsequently adopted in many other plants. The firm also pioneered the production of fish fillets in Ontario. When the firm's headquarters was transferred to Port Dover in 1931 it handled more fish than all other dealers in Port Dover combined and was probably the largest firm on Lake Erie's northern shore. The firm dominated the industry during the late 1930s and 1940s, and its head, Carl Kolbe, was the recognized spokesman of the Lake Erie fishery. By the early 1950s Carl Kolbe had become very pessimistic about the long-term future of the industry. The firm sold most of its fishing fleet in 1954 and adapted its plant to processing poultry. Fishing and packing fish actually became a sideline for the firm before it went bankrupt in 1964.[51]

Although W.F. Kolbe and Company was the most successful of the independent firms of the Erie north shore in the first half of the twentieth century, other independent integrated firms developed and weakened the control of the New York fish merchants. Some of the more prominent firms were the Earleejune Fish Company of Port Maitland, the Eastside Company and the Findlay Fish and Storage Company of Port Stanley, the Goodisons of Erie Beach, Crewe Brothers of Port Crewe, and Maclean Fisheries and Omstead Fisheries of Wheatley. The last of these, Omstead Fisheries, eventually replaced Kolbe and Company as the dominant Canadian fishery on the Great Lakes.

Omstead Fisheries began as a pound-net operation in Wheatley in 1911. On a smaller scale its development followed the pattern set by W.F. Kolbe. In addition to fishing, it expanded into packing, shipping, and processing fish and vegetables. In the 1940s Omstead Fisheries freed itself from the domination of the Peck Slip merchants and emerged as a major buyer in the western end of the lake. In the late 1940s and early 1950s Omstead began two innovations that eventually allowed it to surpass Kolbe and become the dominant firm on the Great Lakes. First, the firm arranged for the distribution of its products by a major grocery store chain, A and P; the arrangement made it completely independent of the traditional fish markets in New York and Chicago. Second, when catches of whitefish and herring fell in the late 1940s, Omstead developed fishing and processing equipment for handling smelt. After Kolbe failed, Omstead was in such a dominant position in the smelt-processing industry that it was able to limit production and support prices through a quota system.[52] Since 1978 Omstead's domination of the Lake Erie fishery has been challenged but not broken by Port Dover's Misener Brothers, who have opened up a market for smelt in Japan.[53]

In spite of the new market in Japan, the United States continues to be the market for well over 90 per cent of Ontario's fish exports; however, control of the actual fishing is now largely in Canadian hands.

Since the withdrawal of Booth Fisheries from Lakes Huron and Superior in 1932–33, no single company has risen to a position of dominance on the two lakes although a number of smaller Canadian fisheries such as the Purvis fishery of Gore Bay and Quebec Harbour, the Nicholl brothers at Port Coldwell, and the Nipigon Bay Fish Company of Rossport have dominated individual ports.[54]

Labour and Working Conditions

Information on labour practices in the fishery is not plentiful. The fishery has always been seasonal, with peaks of productivity and employment during spring and fall spawning runs, a slow period during the hot summer months, and virtual cessation of fishing when the lakes are frozen. A few winter spear fisheries operated through the ice in areas such as Burlington Bay and Toronto Harbour, but they were relatively unimportant. The seine fishery, usually dependent on spring and fall spawning runs, was especially seasonal. A typical example was the Detroit River fishery, which provided two to three months' labour in the autumn and one month's work in the spring.[1] Most of the workers were drawn from local farms. To some extent the farm season and the fishing season meshed, as the Detroit River fall fishery did not begin until September. However, in some cases the two industries competed for the same labour, and on occasion fishing proved more desirable than farming. One official in the Brighton region commented sourly:

> But the moral effect of seine fishing, as it is now carried on, furnishes, perhaps, as grave an objection to its continuance as can be urged, for it is to be found from experience that where it prevails, idleness, drunkeness [sic] and other kindred vices spread with alarming rapidity; and in many respects the population resembles that of a locality where gold has been discovered in small quantities. To such an extent has this demoralizing influence prevailed in some instances, that I have known twice, and even three times the usual wages offered in vain to harvest hands who preferred the chance of a night's fishing to earning an honest penny....[2]

31 Lifting a pound net, ca. 1925.
National Archives of Canada, PA 43252.

Apparently seine fishing was regarded as an agreeable change in routine as well as being potentially profitable.

Seine fisheries were often operated on shares. In Prince Edward County in the 1850s half of the catch went to the owner of the net and half to the crew that operated it.[3] If catches were good, labourers could make much more than they could on farms. How widespread the share system was is not known. At least one of the seine fisheries on the Detroit River was operated on a share basis in the 1890s. The owner, Henry Herbert of Sandwich (now part of Windsor), paid all expenses and took half of the catch. At about the same time, another seine owner at Sandwich paid his crew monthly wages, $30 to $40 per month for common labour and $50 for an overseer. Other seine operators, Mr. Geddes in Toronto Harbour in the 1840s and Thomas Paxton on the Detroit River in the 1830s, also hired their labour.[4]

The pound-net fishery typically enjoyed longer seasons than did the seine fishery. Pound nets were set in the early spring and fished to early summer, when the nets, but not the stakes, were taken out, repaired, and re-tarred. The nets were put back in the water in the late summer and fished until the danger of ice and winter storms, or the close season, required that they be taken out. Peak numbers were employed while the nets were being set and fished. There was also off-season employment. During both the summer break in fishing and the winter some men were employed to repair and tar nets. In the winter, ice was cut and stored. An analysis of the statistical reports of the federal Department of Marine and Fisheries suggests that pound nets could not be operated with less than two men, but there were economies of scale, and a company with 20 nets used proportionately fewer men than a company with only one.

Two Lake Erie pound-net fishermen who appeared before the Dominion Fisheries Commission (1894) gave some details of their operations. One, who fished nine nets with two tugs, employed 12 men at a rate of $35 to $45 per month. The other, who fished eight to ten nets and about 2000 yards of gill net with one tug, employed 3 men year round at annual wages of $450 each and 3 men in season at annual costs of $250 each.[5]

Although detailed records of the pound-net fishery in the nineteenth century are not available, some records of the twentieth-century fishery are. In 1940 W.F. Kolbe and Company paid its pound-netters 30 to 32.5 cents per hour during the fishing season and 25 to 30 cents during the off season.[6] The wage book of one Point Pelee–area pound-net operation shows that of 16 men employed in the years 1947–49, 12 were employed year round. Although wages were entered monthly, they evidently were based on daily or hourly rates and varied from month to month. In January the year-round employees received only $50; in February, April, June, July, September, and October they received $100; in March, May, August, and November they received $125; and in December they received $150. In addition, 11 of the 12 year-round employees received annual bonuses of $700 each.[7] In general, pound-net labourers seem to have been paid salaries; I have found no examples of pound nets being fished on shares. Whether bonuses such as that paid by the Point Pelee fishery were common is not known.

Gill-net fishermen had the longest season of any fishermen. Nets were set as early in the spring as boats could reach open water and were not permanently taken out of the water until late fall. In the nineteenth century the close season for trout and whitefish usually brought the season to an end in early November, but when the close season was abandoned in the twentieth century, boats fished into the new year. Gill-net fishing also provided some winter employment of the same type as pound-net fishing. Nevertheless, few fishermen worked year round at fishing. A 1976 survey of Lake Erie fishermen (not including captains) found that about 48 per cent fished from 31 to 45 weeks of the year; only 5 per cent fished more than 45 weeks.[8] In the off season fishermen found other employment. In the south they were often farmers or farm labourers; in the north they were often lumbermen or trappers.[9]

The size of a gill-net crew varied with the boat type and size. A Mackinaw boat typically operated with a crew of two or three. A steam tug had a captain, an engineer, and a crew of up to five fishermen or deck hands, the number of deck hands varing with the anticipated size of the catch.[10] Additional men were hired to pick fish from the nets during heavy runs.

Gill-net fishermen were paid in a variety of ways: by straight wages, by wages and bonuses, and by various methods of sharing the catch. Because gill-net fishing was less capital intensive than pound-net fishing, a larger proportion of gill-net fishermen were owner/operators than was the case in the pound-net fisheries. Owner/operators sold fish to dealers for cash or, particularly in remote areas in the early years of the fishery, for goods.[11] During the era of corporate concentration a straight wage arrangement was common. A U.S. Fisheries Bureau investigation in 1885 found that the crews of tugs operating out of Cheboygan, Michigan, were paid $25 to $50 per month, engineers were paid $75 to $85, and captains were paid $75 to $100. The investigation also noted that tugs were sometimes rented out or fished on shares.[12] Some of the Buffalo Fish Company's employees on Lake Huron in the 1890s were salaried employees; others worked on a variation of the share system in which the company provided the gear and the fishermen sold the fish to the company at a fixed rate in place of receiving a salary.[13] This system came into general use on the southern shore of Lake Erie in the 1910s and 1920s.[14] On the Canadian side of Lake Erie a straight share system became common early in the twentieth century and is still common today. A 1972 survey of Canadian Lake Erie fishermen found that 72 per cent of their income came from shares.[15] In the 1950s 60 per cent of the catch was allocated to the boat as a replacement and operating fund and 40 per cent to the crew, including the captain even if he was the owner. On modern trawlers the division is usually 50-50.[16] How common the share system was on lakes other than Lake Erie is not known. Shore workers, those involved in repairing nets or processing fish, were paid wages.[17]

American fishermen on the southern shore of Lake Erie began to establish the price they were paid for fish, and hence their wages, by collective bargaining as early as the First World War, and by the 1920s the American Lake Erie fishermen had formed a strong union.[18] Labour in the Canadian fishing industry has never been organized, and it has often been argued that as a result labour costs are lower in Canada than in the United States. A U.S. Tariff Commission survey in 1927 found that Canadian labour costs in the whitefish fishery on Lake Erie were 83 per cent of American costs, and in the lake trout fishery Canadian costs were 56 per cent of American costs.[19] Although labour in the Canadian Great Lakes fishery has never been formally organized, there have been a few strikes. A strike at Rossport in 1922 was apparently a strike by producers for higher prices rather than by labour for higher wages.[20] In 1939 W.F. Kolbe and Company's shore workers and fishermen struck as a result of a wage cut.[21] More recently some of the shore workers of Omstead Fisheries at Wheatley have been organized by the Teamsters Union.

There is a strong tradition of family involvement and continuity in the fishery. Members of the Purvis family have operated a fishery in the Manitoulin Island region since 1879.[22] Omstead Fisheries, founded in 1911, is now in its third generation and employs about 20 family members.[23] There is no evidence of women being directly involved in fishing operations although they have been employed in shore work. Until factory-made nets replaced machine-made nets in the last quarter of the nineteenth century, nets were often made by fishermen's wives and daughters.[24] Subsequently they may have continued to repair nets although there is no evidence of this. So far as is known, women were not involved in the cleaning and processing of fish until the Second World War. To replace men in the services in 1942, W.K. Kolbe employed 30 women to fillet fish.[25]

As is the case with most outdoor occupations, working conditions in the fishery varied with the season and the weather. In the spring and fall, conditions could be harsh and, occasionally, dangerous. Until after World War I most boats were open, and the work of hauling, sorting, and picking nets was done in the open. Gill-net fishermen, because they worked in open water, were particularly exposed to the risks of storms, and tales of storms, wrecks, rescues, and deaths form part of fishery lore. Even in good weather, fishing involved heavy labour. Until 1900, nets were lifted by hand, and except in larger operations, men provided the power for the pile drivers in the pound-net fishery. The hours of work were long. Even today Lake Erie fishermen work more hours per year than the average for Ontario manufacturing employees in spite of the fact that almost 90 per cent of Lake Erie fishermen fish for 45 weeks of the year or less.[26]

Different types of fisheries had different routines. The following description of the day of a Kolbe Company herring boat in 1946 provides some idea of the routine in the gill-net fishery. The tug *Steelhead*, 66 feet long and 16 feet in beam, left Port Dover at 5:00 a.m. After steaming about 30 miles it arrived on the fishing grounds and began lifting nets (using a powered net-lifter), at 8:30. By 11:30 the crew had lifted about 5 miles of nets. As the nets came in, the crew picked the fish, about 2.5 tons of herring, from the

32   A Connibal-type net-lifter, ca. 1915.

'Quebec and Ontario,' in "The Fishing Industry of Canada and Newfoundland," *The Canadian Fisherman*, Vol. 2, No. 9 (Sept. 1915), p. 281.

33   A Crossley-type net-lifter, ca. 1925.

W.N. Koelz, "Fishing Industry of the Great Lakes," in U.S. Bureau of Fisheries, *Report of the United States Commissioner of Fisheries ... 1925*, USGPO, Washington, D.C., 1926, App. 11, Fig. 18.

nets. After the nets were lifted the crew spent about two hours setting dry nets. On the trip back to port they finished picking the nets they had lifted that morning, cleaned them, and stowed them in boxes, and then cleaned the tug. When the boat arrived back at port in the late afternoon the shore crew packed the fish, iced them, and loaded them for shipment to New York.[27] In smaller fisheries than Kolbe's this shore work might have been the responsibility of the fishing crew. Depending on the company, the shore crew or the fishing crew might also be responsible for repairing nets and doing related work. Major net repairs were winter work but minor repairs were done daily, and before the introduction of nylon nets, wet nets had to be placed on drying reels daily. In some fisheries the crew also cleaned fish on the way back to port.

Although the fisherman's day was often long, it was unusual for a boat to remain on the fishing grounds overnight. Most fishermen lived in small and medium-sized towns such as Port Dover or Collingwood, and their life ashore was little different from that of other town dwellers. In some cases fishermen lived in tiny rural communities, such as Port Crewe, that were entirely devoted to fishing, and in other cases fisheries were operated in conjunction with farms; this is still the case around the Bay of Quinte.

In the nineteenth and early twentieth centuries many of the fishing communities on northern Lake Huron and Lake Superior were seasonal camps rather than permanent communities. For example, Quebec Harbour on Michipicoten Island, Squaw Island on Georgian Bay, and Main Duck Island on Lake Ontario were only occupied seasonally. Fishermen, sometimes accompanied by their families, arrived at the camps in the early spring and left in the late fall to return to their homes. Living conditions in the camps were necessarily more primitive than in the settled communities. Some were simply a group of men's bunkhouses, but others were more elaborate. At Squaw Island, a remote but important camp, there were enough families to support a school and a Presbyterian summer mission. With improvements in transportation and changes in fishing patterns, the seasonal camps have largely disappeared.

The physical plant needed to operate a fishery varied with its location, the type of fishery, the period in which it operated, and the degree to which the fishery was vertically integrated. Some fishermen simply caught fish and consigned them to a market, contracting with other firms to pack, process, and ship the fish. Some firms were involved in fishing, packing, and shipping, but did little if any processing. A few firms, including the largest, were involved in fishing, packing, processing, and shipping. The shore facilities owned by a fishery would reflect its level of integration.

34 Men transferring a net from a drying reel to a small reel that would be mounted in the stern of a boat. Setting nets from small reels was a technique peculiar to Lake Ontario.

Photo by C.M. Johnston. National Archives of Canada, PA 57816.

35 A fishing camp on Fitzwilliam Island, Georgian Bay, pre-1902.

Ontario. Dept. of Fisheries, *Fourth Annual Report ... 1902* (Toronto: L.K. Cameron, King's Printer, 1903), p. 15; National Library of Canada, NL 13106.

36　Unloading herring at Kolbe's dock, Port Dover, 1914.
D.A. Buscombe, *Port Dover Scenes*, Vol. 1, Through Changing Times, 1860–1974 (Port Stanley, Ont.: Erie Shore Publications, [1974]), p. 150; National Library of Canada, NL 13506.

In the simplest form a seine fishery required little more than a boat to set the seine, the seine itself, and men to haul it. It is doubtful if any fixed shore facilities were required except perhaps a twine shed in which to store and repair the net and other tools. If fish were sold fresh locally, then no means of processing or preserving them was necessary. If they were salted, then sheds for storing salt, assembling barrels, and cleaning fish were required. Given that the fishery was only followed during three to four months of the year, the structures were usually of a simple and inexpensive frame design.

A fully integrated fishery in the late nineteenth century would have required a more elaborate plant than an early seine fishery. At a minimum it would have had a net shed, fish house, and icehouse in addition to boats, docks, and nets. Twine sheds were used for assembling, repairing, and storing nets and related equipment. Because nets were stretched out when they were being made or repaired, the sheds had to be comparatively long; one owned by C.W. Gauthier at French River was 90 feet in length.[28]

In the fish house, workers prepared fish for shipment to market. Depending on the type of fish, the market for which they were destined, and the practice of the fishery, fish might be shipped in the round, eviscerated, fresh, frozen, or salted. At many Lake Erie ports fish were shipped fresh in the round, and the principal activity in the fish house would have been sorting fish by type and size and packing them on ice in boxes. During the 1920s some Lake Erie fishermen began to fillet fish. On the upper lakes fish were more likely to be dressed prior to being packed and shipped. Salting fish declined in importance as a preservative technique after 1890, but in some areas it persisted as late as the 1930s.

A fish house was an essential part of any integrated fishery. In a fishery that had a freezing plant, it is probable that the fish house and its activities would be incorporated in the plant. In some pound-net fisheries on Lake Erie and southern Lake Huron, the catch was transferred directly from the nets to waiting boats that took it to plants in the United States. The Americans provided ice and containers, and the Canadian fishermen would have required neither fish houses nor icehouses. Similarly on the North Channel in the 1890s many small fishermen delivered fish from their nets to depots established by larger firms such as Noble Brothers. The larger firms provided ice and containers and took responsibility for packing and shipping.[29] The only equipment that the primary producer had to have was a boat, nets, and a twine shed.

By the twentieth century, icehouses were essential parts of all but the most basic fisheries. Although we have very little information on icehouses actually used, there is no reason to believe they would have been any different from those used in other industries. Essentially they were well-insulated buildings for storing ice through the summer months. Because most fisheries would have used natural ice from the lakes, icehouses were located as close to the water as possible.

Freezers, as opposed to icehouses, were not a part of most fisheries in Ontario prior to the 1920s. Freezing began in major American fishing ports, Sandusky, Ohio, and Erie, Pennsylvania, as early as the 1870s, but most Canadian fish were salted or exported fresh on ice. A freezer was built at Southampton in 1879, and there were freezers at Collingwood, Meaford, Wiarton, and the Duck Islands on Lake Huron in the mid-1890s. By 1930 there were freezers in most major ports.[30]

In addition to a fish house, twine shed, and icehouse, most fisheries would have had a number of ancilliary structures. In 1910 the Crewe Brothers established a fishery in a rural area on the shore of Lake Erie. Initially it consisted of two structures that combined icehouse, fish house, twine house, and dwelling. As their business grew it became a small settlement, Port Crewe. By 1942 Crewe Brothers owned three large dwellings and

37 Port Dover, 1920.

D.A. Buscombe, *Port Dover Scenes*, Vol. 1, Through Changing Times, 1860–1974 (Port Stanley, Ont.:
Erie Shore Publications, [1974]), p. 141; National Library of Canada, NL 13503.

38 Port Stanley, 1923.

National Archives of Canada, PA 31224.

six small ones, a new twine house, a hay barn/stable, a blacksmith shop, a garage, a fish house, and an icehouse. The site included a large grassy field on which pound nets were spread to dry. As Port Crewe was not on a natural harbour, its boats operated directly from the beach and when not in use were hoisted out of the water with chain hoists. In addition, because the beach was backed by a 75-foot clay bank, an inclined railway moved fish, ice, and supplies from the beach to the fish house.[31]

The Crewe Brothers fishery was located in the countryside. Fisheries located in towns would not have provided residences for their employees and might have hired the services of blacksmiths and draymen rather than maintain their own smithies, stables, and garages.

In general the buildings that housed the fishery were simply built frame structures. Indeed, judging from many of the photographs, they were roughly built, and this is especially true of the structures, probably viewed as temporary, in the fishing camps. However, there were exceptions. For example, at the Goodison fishery at Erie Beach and the Crewe Brothers fishery, major structures were built of brick or cement block and there were substantial frame structures in some of the larger ports. Nevertheless, most of the buildings that housed the early fishery were small and simple, and have generally disappeared.

Changes in Fish Stocks

Increased marketing opportunities led to increases in fishing intensity; that is, more manpower and equipment were used and more effective techniques were adopted. The number of fishermen on the Canadian Great Lakes rose from less than 2000 in 1879 to more than 3200 shortly after the First World War. Improved equipment meant that fishing intensity rose more rapidly than manpower. In 1881 there were less than 1 million yards of gill nets licensed for use on the Canadian side of the lakes and 74 pound nets. By the mid-1890s there were 3.5 million yards of gill nets and 400 pound nets licensed. In fact, the figures for licensed gear in the 1890s understate the amount of fishing because gill-net fisherman frequently fished twice as much gear as they were licenced to use.[1] The figures for pound nets are probably more accurate, but they do not take into account the frequent use of illegal trap nets. Fishing intensity continued to increase until at least 1930 when over 1000 pound nets and 6.4 million yards of gill nets were licensed. As a result of these increases, the reported catch per man rose from about 5700 pounds in 1880 to 10 000 pounds in 1890. It remained at roughly this level until about the First World War, and then began to decline slowly until the 1940s. The decline in productivity was only reversed in the 1950s when a declining labour force in combination with large catches of low-value smelt raised productivity. Today the catch is about 36 000 pounds per man. On Lake Erie, where the least labour-intensive form of fishing (trawling) is widely used, the catch per man is about 66 000 pounds; on Lake Ontario it is only 6600 pounds per man.

The immense increase in fishing intensity, plus environmental changes, put an increasing strain on fish stocks. The Atlantic salmon was the first fish to be affected by the changed conditions. They were clearly endangered by the early 1860s and, despite efforts to stock them artificially, were extinct by 1900. Although fishing may have been a factor in the extinction of the salmon, it is now believed that the decisive factor was the loss of their spawning grounds as a result of the blocking of streams by milldams, and the silting and reduced summer flow of streams as a result of deforestation.[2]

The lake sturgeon was the second fish to be endangered. Until the 1860s, sturgeon were considered a nuisance. They were not desired as food fish and, because they were very large, they often damaged nets when they became entangled in them. As a result, when they were caught they were destroyed but not used. During the 1860s the techniques for processing sturgeon eggs as caviar and for smoking sturgeon flesh were introduced into North America, and the sturgeon suddenly became a highly prized commercial fish. Sturgeon do not mature until they are 20 to 25 years of age and the population could not support the intensive fishing that resulted from its popularity. The catch peaked in the mid-1880s and fell off quickly. By 1900, sturgeon were no longer commercially significant in the Great Lakes. In the twentieth century various steps such as closed seasons have been taken to protect them, but they remain rare.[3]

The effect of heavy fishing and environmental change was not so dramatic on fish that formed the backbone of the Great Lakes commercial fishery prior to the 1920s: lake whitefish, lake trout, and lake herring or cisco. Although there were notable declines in some species in some lakes, the total annual catch of all fish remained within the 25-million- to 35-million-pound range from the late 1880s to 1950. However, the relative stability was only maintained by constantly increased fishing intensity; there was also a marked shift from the most desirable fish — whitefish and trout — to less desirable fish — first herring, and about the time of the First World War, yellow perch, walleye, northern pike, and sauger.

The shift to less commercially desirable fish was especially pronounced after the collapse of the herring fishery in Lake Erie in 1925. From 1915 to 1924 the average Canadian catch of herring was about 8.7 million pounds, equal to about 50 per cent of the catch for all species in Lake Erie. In the following decade the herring catch averaged only 1.1 million pounds, less than 10 per cent of the total Lake Erie catch. With the exception of a brief revival of the herring fishery in 1946–47, herring catches have remained low and now form a negligible part of the Lake Erie fishery.

The exact cause of the collapse of the herring fishery is unknown. J. Van Oosten, a scientist with the U.S. fisheries services, placed the principal blame for the collapse on overfishing, particularly on the use of the bull net. T.H. Langlois, an Ohio researcher in the 1940s, suggested that the primary

39 Herring tugs at Port Arthur, Ontario, in 1915. Part of the dock is
covered with fresh herring, and the barrels on the scow
contain pickled herring.
'Quebec and Ontario,' in "The Fishing Industry of Canada and Newfoundland," *The Canadian
Fisherman*, Vol. 2, No. 9 (Sept. 1915), p. 282.

cause of the collapse was a relatively short-term increase in suspended sedi-
ments in the water that, combined with heavy fishing, drove the herring
population below a critical threshold. Even more recently it has been argued
that there may have been a relationship between the appearance of rainbow
smelt in the Great Lakes and the decline of herring.[4]

From 1925, when the herring disappeared, to the late 1950s the Lake Erie
fishery depended on a variety of fish: the sauger, walleye, whitefish, white
bass, and principally, yellow perch. During the 1940s, smelt became increasingly common but were not harvested on a large scale until the late
1950s when trawl nets were introduced on the Great Lakes. Trawling made
fishing for smelt more lucrative and since 1960 smelt have become a major
component in the Lake Erie fishery. They now constitute over half of the
total weight of the catch on Lake Erie. Largely because of the tremendous
growth of the smelt fishery, the total catch in the Canadian waters of Lake
Erie is now about 43 million pounds per year, three times what it was during

and after World War I in what are traditionally viewed as the best years of the fishery.

Until the 1890s the Canadian fishery on Lake Huron was larger than the Canadian Lake Erie fishery. It peaked at about 14 million pounds per year in 1890 and then fell behind the Lake Erie fishery. From 1900 to 1940 it maintained its yield at from 6 to 8 million pounds per year; lake trout accounted for about 3 to 5 million pounds of the total and whitefish accounted for about 1.5 million pounds. Herring were not a significant factor. During the 1940s the whitefish catch fell to about 750 000 pounds. Although there was a strong recovery of the whitefish fishery from 1950 to 1955, it fell off again in 1956 and has never fully recovered. The reason for its collapse is not known although the failure of the American whitefish industry in Lake Huron, which occurred in the late 1930s and was even more complete than the collapse of the Canadian fishery, has been blamed on the use of deep trap nets.[5] Trap nets were not legal in Canada during the 1930s. It seems possible that the introduction of nylon netting in Lake Huron in the late 1940s may have increased effective fishing intensity and resulted in overfishing. As well, the failure of the Lake Huron trout fishery in the late 1940s and early 1950s resulted in increased concentration on whitefish.[6] Finally, although sea lamprey preyed on large lake trout, once the lake trout were destroyed they attacked the next available large fish, the whitefish, and may have contributed to its decline.

The lake trout fishery in Lake Huron also failed in the 1940s. The collapse is attributed almost entirely to the depredations of the sea lamprey. Although lamprey have been brought under control by the work of the Great Lakes Fishery Commission, the trout have not recovered. No substitutes for lake trout and whitefish were readily available, and the total catch in Lake Huron declined through the 1940s, 1950s, and 1960s. It reached a low of about 2.4 million pounds in 1972 and has since recovered to about 4 million pounds per year. About 40 per cent of the catch is whitefish; the other important species are yellow perch and walleye.

Although Lake Superior is much the largest of the Great Lakes, it is deep, cold, and relatively unproductive. The catch peaked at 8 217 000 pounds in 1915 and since then has generally been between two and four million pounds. Lake trout formed the original basis of the industry with a small but steady production of whitefish that has continued up to the present. Since 1915, herring have been an important part of the catch. The lake trout fishery failed in the 1950s as a result of the invasion of sea lampreys although the failure was not as complete as in Lake Huron. Since reaching a low of under 100 000 pounds in 1962, the annual catch of lake trout has

40   Dressing Lake Trout at Jackfish, Lake Superior, ca. 1930.
National Archives of Canada, PA 43267.

risen slowly to about 400 000 pounds. Lake herring have supplied over half of the total catch since the lake trout failed.

Since the 1920s Lake Ontario has generally reported the smallest catch of all the Great Lakes and since the 1890s its catch has generally been the least valuable in dollars. It is possible that the best days of its fishery, when salmon and whitefish were abundant, predated the first statistical records of the fishery. From the 1880s to 1920, herring formed the basis of the fishery, followed by whitefish and lake trout. Whitefish were the dominant species caught in the 1920s, and herring enjoyed a brief revival from 1936 to 1941, but with these exceptions the Lake Ontario fishery before 1950 was composed more or less equally of herring, whitefish, lake trout, northern pike, catfish, and yellow perch. Trout and herring declined and then disappeared in the 1940s and 1950s, and whitefish declined during the 1960s. Today the catch, which totals about two million pounds, is composed principally of catfish, eel, sunfish, and white and yellow perch.

Post-Confederation
Legislation, Management
and Conservation

At Confederation the federal government assumed responsibility for the Great Lakes fishery under section 91, subsection 12, of the British North America Act, which gave the central government legislative jurisdiction over sea coast and inland fisheries. It retained primary responsibility for the fishery until 1899 when it delegated most of its responsibility to Ontario. In 1868 the federal government established the Department of Marine and Fisheries and passed a new fishery act. The act refined and extended the provisions of the act of 1858, but did not introduce any new principles. Enforcement of existing legislation was the first priority of the new department, but despite an increase in paid fishery officers from 23 in 1868 to 90 in 1896, enforcement continued to be the major weakness.

In part, the failure to enforce fisheries laws adequately was a result of poor pay and inadequate equipment. Appointments were political and were made on the recommendation of the local member of Parliament. One Conservative member commented, after having recommended his brother and another man for appointment as fishing overseers on Lake Superior, "I don't consider that you pay sufficient salaries [\$200 to \$300 per year was being offered] to get good men to do the work."[1] His judgement was sound, for his brother was removed from office four years later (by a Liberal administration) for "inefficiency and neglect of duty." The brother was suspected of favouring the local agent of the fish trust.[2]

41 The patrol boat *Vigilant*.
National Archives of Canada, PA 159651.

Inadequate equipment was also a problem. Until 1888, patrols were conducted in rowboats or sailboats although fishermen began using steam tugs in the 1870s. The department acquired its first steam patrol boat in 1888, but did not get a second boat until 1892.[3] Thereafter there were usually two and sometimes three major patrol boats on the Great Lakes. The acquisition of powered patrol boats did improve enforcement, but the boats were still too few to cover the vast areas of the Great Lakes and in some cases were unsuited to the work. For example, in 1893 Fishery Overseer F. Kerr had to hire a local fishing tug to investigate fisheries in the Wheatley area because the department's boat, the *Dolphin*, was too leaky and unseaworthy to be taken out in rough weather.[4] The *Vigilant*, on the other hand, was a large, fast, and seaworthy vessel; it was, in fact, suitable to be a small warship. Its size and distinctive lines were its greatest weakness as it was easily recognized at a great distance and American poachers could often escape across the boundary before the *Vigilant* reached them.[5] In 1921 the *Vigilant* was replaced by three smaller vessels.

Although equipment and pay were problems, the main obstacles to full enforcement of regulations were political. In many cases fishery officials were either unwilling or unable to enforce regulations directly related to the fishery. For example, it was generally accepted that the dumping of mill wastes into streams damaged spawning grounds and harmed the fishery, and laws preventing pollution by mill wastes were first passed in the 1840s. From at least the time of Confederation, fishery officials attempted to curb the dumping of mill wastes, but the political power of the lumber industry was able to prevent any effective reforms until at least the turn of the century.[6] In another case, Fishery Officer A. Holmes reported in 1888 that almost without exception, fishermen used double the 6000 yards of gill nets that their licences allowed and that they generally used 4.5-inch net rather than the legal 5-inch net. The use of more net than was permitted under licence continued to be a common and tacitly accepted practice well into the 1890s.[7] In fact, according to a study of the Lake Erie fishery conducted in 1980, Lake Erie fishermen continue to use many more gill nets than their licences allow.[8]

It was particularly difficult to enforce regulations where Canadian fishermen were in close contact and competition with American fishermen, who were perceived to be less subject to regulations. A close season on whitefish in November and December was instituted by the first Dominion Fisheries Act in 1868, but prior to 1890 it was never enforced on the Detroit River system where Canadians fished within sight of American fishermen.[9] In 1890 the department began enforcing the act, but area fishermen complained that the department was ruining them. By 1896 they had gained enough support from local citizens and politicians to have the regulations suspended. The suspension was temporary, but Detroit River fishermen were usually able to gain suspension of the regulations annually until the close season was finally abolished in 1915. The local fishermen would apply to the commissioner of fisheries, E.E. Prince, for an extension of the fishing season. Prince would refuse, the fishermen would apply to their members of Parliament, the members would approach the minister, and in most years the minister would overrule Prince and grant an extension of the season.[10]

Fishery officials did act vigorously to enforce some regulations such as the prohibition on trap nets. Trap nets were regularly seized and destroyed in Georgian Bay, but fishery officials reported that the nets were quickly replaced by the large fish-packing firms and that no real reduction in the number of illegal nets was achieved.[11] Fishery officials also acted against American fishing in Canadian waters. American nets and boats were seized and boats were occasionally fired on. On one occasion when a tug refused to surrender, it was run down and two fishermen drowned.[12]

Perhaps the most important long-term initiative made by the federal government during the period in which it was primarily responsible for the fishery was the acquisition of a fish hatchery at Newcastle, Ontario, in 1868. The idea of artificial propagation was not new. Its origins in Europe can be traced back to the eighteenth century, and the first government-operated fish hatchery had been established in France in 1850. In North America a number of small private hatcheries were established in the 1850s and 1860s. In Quebec the superintendent of fisheries had carried out experimental hatching in 1857 and 1858, but his work did not develop into a full-scale hatchery.[13]

In Ontario Samuel Wilmot, a farmer and merchant at Newcastle, became interested in the possibility of restoring the Atlantic salmon in Lake Ontario to its previous abundance through artificial propagation. Salmon were particularly vulnerable to overfishing when they congregated in spawning streams. In addition, the damming of spawning streams and siltation and reduced summer flow as a result of deforestation reduced their habitat. By the 1860s they were quite rare in most of their former spawning streams. In 1865 or 1866 Wilmot established a small salmon hatchery on his farm at Newcastle. In 1868 the government leased the hatchery and hired him to operate it.[14] In 1876 Wilmot was made superintendent of fish culture and charged with expanding the hatchery system. By the time he retired in 1894 there were 15 hatcheries in Canada; the 3 Ontario hatcheries produced whitefish and some lake trout. The expansion of the hatchery system continued after his retirement until by 1926 there were 8 federal and 7 provincial hatcheries in Ontario alone.[15]

The rapid expansion of the hatchery system in Ontario was matched by equally rapid development of hatcheries in the states bordering the Great Lakes. The growth was based largely on a belief in the efficiency of the hatchery system compared to natural propagation. It was believed that under natural conditions only a very small proportion, perhaps 1 per cent, of all whitefish eggs were fertilized and that only a fraction of fertilized eggs developed to maturity. Hatcheries were able to fertilize from 75 to 80 per cent of the eggs they received and were then able to raise a larger proportion of eggs to the stage at which the fry were released. One researcher in 1908 calculated that hatcheries were 750 times more efficient than nature.[16] Given the advantage of this efficiency, it was believed that hatcheries could

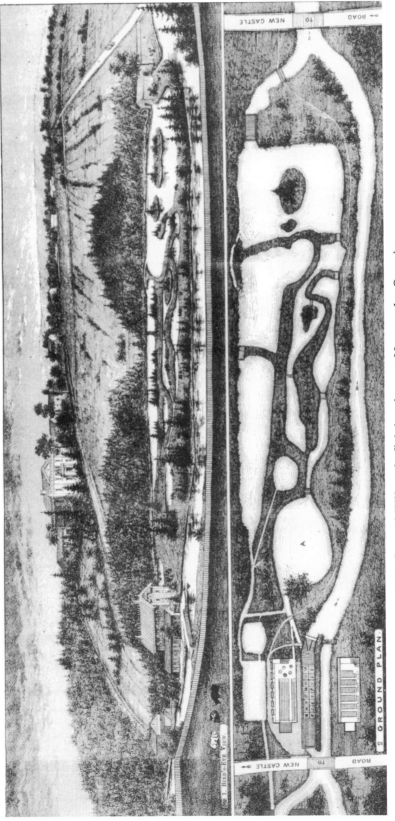

42 Samuel Wilmot's fish hatchery at Newcastle, Ontario.

Canada. Dept. of Marine and Fisheries, *Tenth Annual Report … 1877*, "Report of the Commissioner of Fisheries…," (Ottawa: MacLean, Roger & Co., 1878), App. 2, Report on Fish-Breeding in the Dominion of Canada, 1877, facing p. 3.

counterbalance the loss of spawning grounds, pollution, and overfishing. Early in this century some fishery experts suggested that, given sufficient hatcheries, the closed season during the spawning period would no longer be necessary.[17]

Although there was widespread support for the hatchery system from both commercial fishermen and fishery officials, scientists were unable to prove that large-scale planting of fish increased the commercial catch. The case of the Lake Ontario salmon was not encouraging. After the establishment of the hatchery at Newcastle in 1868, the salmon made a small but short-lived recovery, and after 1880 the government gave up trying to save them and concentrated on raising whitefish and lake trout.[18] W.F. Whitcher, the commissioner of fisheries and Wilmot's superior, argued that although the technical operation of fertilizing eggs and raising fish was a success, there was no evidence that planting had affected the commercial catch.[19] In spite of these doubts the hatchery system was greatly expanded. In 1927, after the provincial government had taken over the federal hatcheries in Ontario, 714 128 206 fry were planted; of these, 448 789 750 were whitefish.[20] Plantings continued on the same scale for 30 years, but seemed to have no discernible relation to whitefish catches, which had peaked on Lake Superior in 1885, on Lake Huron in 1892, and on Lake Ontario in 1924, and which would peak on Lake Erie in 1949.

During the 1920s the Biological Board of Canada carried out a number of studies that found no provable relationship between plantings and catch. Similar studies were carried out by different state fishery commissions with similar results. The consensus developed by this reappraisal was that traditional fish-culture methods had been of little or no benefit to the commercial fishery. There was an immense mortality among the extremely small fish that hatcheries normally planted. Small populations of parent fish could produce very large numbers of fry if several favourable environmental factors coincided. On the other hand, very large parent classes, or large plantings of fry, would produce small numbers of fry if all environmental factors were not favourable. The conclusion drawn from these findings was that hatcheries were only useful in special situations such as introducing new species to lakes or restoring stocks, such as the lake trout, that had been reduced by a predator.[21]

Although these findings did not support stocking large numbers of commercial fish, Ontario hatcheries continued to produce about 500 million fish annually to the 1950s. Over half of these were whitefish. It was only in the late 1960s that the breeding of whitefish was stopped and the entire hatchery program greatly reduced. In 1980–81 only 7.5 million fry were planted, less than one per cent of the number planted in some years in the 1920s and 1940s.[22]

In conjunction with attempts to restore depleted stocks of indigenous fish, fishery departments in both Canada and the United States introduced new species to the Great Lakes. In some cases new species were intended to replace indigenous species, such as the salmon, that had been lost; in other cases they were intended to fill perceived gaps in the fish community. As early as 1873–74, attempts were made to replace the Atlantic salmon in Lake Ontario with salmon from California.[23] Salmon were also introduced to the upper Great Lakes. The initial attempts were failures. More recent attempts in the 1950s and 1960s have had limited success and there are now small, self-sustaining populations of pink salmon in all the lakes. In addition, coho and chinook salmon are regularly stocked and grow to maturity but do not reproduce.[24] Whether the introduced salmon are numerous enough to support commercial fishing is hotly debated; up to the present they have been reserved for the sport fishery.

Only two deliberately introduced exotic species, carp and smelt, have been successful commercially. Carp had been raised in ponds in Europe since the Middle Ages and was an esteemed food fish. It was probably introduced into North America about 1830, but did not become common in the wild until the U.S. Bureau of Fisheries began to plant it in 1877.[25] The Canadian government also raised carp at the Newcastle hatchery from about 1881.[26] The fish quickly became established in the Great Lakes, but did not become a popular food fish in North America and by the 1890s was considered by many authorities to be a nuisance. It was believed to eat spawn and to ruin spawning beds for more valuable fish. In 1896 the Canadian fishery commissioner, E.E. Prince, denounced it scornfully and stated that its "propagation in Canadian waters is little short of a crime."[27] In spite of his scorn the carp throve and continues to be an important minor item in the commercial fishery.

The other successful exotic, rainbow smelt, was probably introduced into Lake Michigan about 1912.[28] It did not become common in the other lakes until the 1940s and was of little commercial significance until the early 1960s, when new fishing and processing techniques made its capture commercially rewarding. It is now one of the mainstays of the Lake Erie fishery.

Three other exotic species, the alewife, sea lamprey, and white perch, have appeared in the lakes within the historical period and have affected the commercial fishery. The alewife may have been native to Lake Ontario or may have migrated there via the Erie Canal or St. Lawrence River. It was first identified in Lake Ontario in 1873 and appeared in the upper lakes in the 1930s. It has since become so common that it has been blamed for contributing to the decline of more valuable fish. It is of no commercial value except on Lake Michigan, where millions of pounds are processed as pet food and fish meal.[29]

The sea lamprey may have been indigenous to Lake Ontario, but it was not identified in Lake Erie until 1921 and not in the other upper lakes until a decade later.[30] Its proliferation in Lakes Huron, Michigan, and Superior coincided with, and was a principal cause of, the calamitous decline of the lake trout fishery in the upper lakes in the 1950s. Although the lamprey population has been brought under control, the lake trout fishery has not been restored. One aspect of the program to restore the lake trout fishery has involved attempts to introduce the splake, a cross between lake trout and speckled trout.[31]

White perch appeared in Lake Ontario about 1950, probably by way of the Oswego River. By the 1970s they constituted about 17 per cent of the Lake Ontario catch.[32]

Successful fishery management using tools such as closed seasons, catch limits, hatcheries, and the introduction of new species is dependent on detailed knowledge of fish and their habitat. At the time the Canadian government became actively involved in fishery management, very little had been done in the field and the early fishery officials learned as they went. Although many of the men, notably Samuel Wilmot, were competent, they were without formal training in fishery science and it was not until 1892 that a trained scientist was appointed to the Fishery Branch.

Edward Prince, a fishery specialist, was a professor of zoology at St. Mungo's College, Glasgow, prior to being appointed commissioner and general inspector of fisheries in 1892, a position he held until 1923.[33] In addition to his administrative work he did fishery research and published scientific papers. While he held the position of commissioner the Dominion government undertook two major surveys of fisheries in Ontario. One, headed by Samuel Wilmot, surveyed the fisheries throughout the Great Lakes in the early 1890s; the other, on which Prince served, investigated the fisheries in Georgian Bay between 1905 and 1908. In addition the department participated with the United States in a survey of the fisheries in the boundary waters in the early 1890s.

Prince's most lasting achievement was the organization of a board of management for a marine biological station in 1898. The board, known after 1912 as the Biological Board of Canada and after 1937 as the Fisheries Research Board of Canada, was responsible for organizing and co-ordinating fishery research in Canada.[34] It established research stations on the Atlantic and Pacific coasts, and in 1904 took over the management of a research station at Go Home Bay on Georgian Bay. The Go Home Bay station was operated until about 1914 when it was closed, possibly as part of the federal government's policy of withdrawing from the management of the Ontario fishery.[35] The federal government did not carry on fishery research in Ontario again until 1956, when it established a research station at London, Ontario.

After the federal government's withdrawal there was no formal fishery research establishment in Ontario, aside from the hatcheries, until 1925. In 1925 the provincial government appointed a biologist and organized a Biological and Fish Culture Branch.[36] It now maintains fishery research stations at Glenora and Maple on Lake Ontario, Wheatley on Lake Erie, South Baymouth on Lake Huron, and Thunder Bay on Lake Superior. The federal government resumed research on the Great Lakes fishery in 1956 in response to the threat posed by the sea lamprey. Initially federal research was confined to lamprey control, but under a series of federal-provincial agreements, federal research was expanded to include limnological research, research on product development and on handling, packaging, preparation, and storage techniques, and economic studies.[37]

Federal and Provincial
Jurisdictions

Constitutional and international matters have affected the management of the fishery. Under section 91 of the British North America Act the federal government assumed complete responsibility for managing all fisheries in the Dominion including that of the Great Lakes. The responsibility was exercised by the Department of Marine and Fisheries under the Fisheries Act of 1868.

The federal government's confident assertion of its authority over all fisheries received a check in 1882 as a result of a court case, Robertson v. Regina. In 1874 the government had leased a salmon fishery on the Mirimachi River to A.C. Robertson. The land bordering the leased fishery had been granted to the Nova Scotia and New Brunswick Land Company in 1835 by the colony of New Brunswick, and in 1875 the company gave permission to J. Steadman and E. Hanson to fish the Mirimachi within its grant. Robertson, on the basis of his lease, ejected them from the fishery and was sued for damages. The Supreme Court of New Brunswick decided against Robertson on the grounds that his lease was invalid, and Robertson then sued the crown for the loss of his fishing privileges and for his legal expenses. The Supreme Court of Canada ruled that although the Parliament of Canada had power to regulate and protect inland fisheries, the minister of Marine and Fisheries could only grant licences or leases to fish where the exclusive right of fishing did not already exist by law.[1] In general the exclusive right of fishing belonged to the owners of land bordering the streams or rivers. In the case of crown lands in the old provinces, this meant the provincial and not the federal government; hence in most cases the federal government had no right to license fishing on rivers.

It was not immediately clear to what extent the Robertson case affected federal control of inland fisheries. For example, did it apply to major navigable streams, such as the Detroit River, that were also boundary waters? Or to the Great Lakes? Whatever its ultimate application, the Robertson case encouraged several provinces to challenge federal control of the fisheries.

In 1885 Ontario passed a fisheries act that in many respects paralleled the federal act.[2] It provided for the issue of licences and leases by the commissioner of Crown Lands, for the appointment of fishery overseers, for the issue of regulations by the lieutenant-governor-in-council, and for the setting aside of areas for natural or artificial propagation of fish. The act was specifically limited to fisheries for which Ontario had the right to legislate, a provision that prevented it from being disallowed by the federal government on the grounds that it was ultra vires, but recognized the possibility of the provincial jurisdiction's extension through judicial interpretation.

Initially Ontario does not seem to have implemented the provisions of its fisheries act, but in 1887 it published specific regulations by order-in-council and appointed three fishery overseers to enforce them. The regulations encroached on what the federal government considered its prerogative and in some cases were at odds with federal regulations, but conflict between the two jurisdictions was avoided by an understanding that Ontario would limit its jurisdiction to the smaller inland lakes and non-navigable streams. The understanding lasted only to the early 1890s when the federal government re-asserted its right to control the smaller lakes and streams and Ontario began to appoint fishery overseers on the Great Lakes.[3]

From 1887 to 1897 Ontario's fishery overseers reported to the commissioner of Crown Lands. In 1890, as a result of increasing concern over the decline of both game and fish in Ontario, the provincial government appointed a commission to investigate game and fish resources and to make recommendations for their preservation. The commission reported that Ontario's game and fish laws were largely unenforced and recommended the appointment of a permanent commission to make enforcement more effective.[4] A permanent commission was appointed, but because of the divided jurisdiction over the fishery, it largely confined itself to enforcing the game laws. It did, however, make use of its annual reports to point out the deficiencies of federal fishery management.

Increasing pressure from Ontario and other provinces forced the federal government to seek resolution of the jurisdictional questions relating to the fishery, and in 1894–95 it referred 17 questions to the Supreme Court. The results were then appealed to the Judicial Committee of the Privy Council. The Privy Council's ruling in 1898 confirmed the federal government's right to legislate for the protection of inland fisheries. In particular the federal government had the right to regulate the manner of taking fish. At the same time the Privy Council ruled that the provincial governments retained all the proprietary rights to the fisheries that they had held at Confederation. In general the provinces had the exclusive right to license fisheries; they could also attach conditions to the licences if they wished. The Privy Council recognized that divided jurisdiction could lead to difficulties, but relied on the "good sense" of the governments involved to solve any problems that arose.[5]

As a result of the ruling the federal government turned over responsibility for licensing Ontario fisheries, including those on the Great Lakes, to the provincial government in the spring of 1899. At the same time it delegated responsibility for the enforcement of federal regulations to the province and dismissed its enforcement staff with the exception of three officers who were retained to carry out general supervision of the regulations. It also kept one boat to patrol the international border on the Great Lakes.[6] Ontario organized a Fisheries Branch under the Attorney General's department and appointed a staff of fishery overseers to replace the federal officers. In 1907 the Fisheries Branch was amalgamated with the Board of Game Commissioners under a superintendent of Game and Fisheries.[7]

Although the federal government had largely abandoned responsibility for enforcement of fishery regulations in Ontario, it retained its responsibility for legislation. When the Ontario government established fishery regulations that included closed seasons and catch limits in 1899, the federal government objected that the regulations were ultra vires.[8] A similar reaction greeted the Ontario Fisheries Act of 1900. The Ontario government repealed the portions of the act that had established regulations on the understanding that the federal government would enact regulations to replace them.[9] However, no agreement could be reached as to what the regulations should be. Over the next decade relations between the federal and Ontario fishery departments became increasingly bitter. Provincial authorities accused federal authorities of failing to enact adequate regulations; in particular the provincial superintendent of fisheries attacked the federal decision to end the closed season for whitefish in certain areas. For their part, federal officials accused provincial officers of failing to enforce existing federal regulations. In 1908 the federal government considered reassuming direct responsibility for enforcing its regulations.[10]

The deadlock between the two levels of government was broken about 1911–12. The reason for the change is not clear although a compromise may have been made possible by the existence of Conservative administrations in both Toronto and Ottawa after 1911. The federal government continued to enact fishery legislation and pass regulations for Ontario, but it consulted closely with the provincial government on the content of the legislation and regulations. Over a period of years provincial input increased to the point where the federal role was reduced to that of a rubber stamp; in 1938 a provincial spokesman stated that in 12 years not a single request for a change in regulations had been refused by the federal government.[11]

As a part of its program to transfer responsibilities for regulating the fishery to Ontario, the federal government also withdrew the three fishery officers it had kept in Ontario since 1899. In 1922 federal fishery patrols ended on the Great Lakes.

The federal government also began to reduce its commitment to hatcheries in Ontario after 1912. Following the original acquisition of a hatchery at Newcastle in 1868, hatcheries had been restablished at Sandwich (1876), Ottawa (1890), Belleville (1901), and Sarnia and Wiarton (1908). When Ontario assumed an increased responsibility for, and collected the revenue from, the fishery after 1898, the federal government found it difficult to justify expenditures on hatcheries. In 1912 the provincial government agreed to take responsibility for hatching game fish in Ontario, and the federal government agreed to continue breeding fish for the commercial fishery. As a result the federal government closed four hatcheries between 1912 and 1914. However, it opened six new hatcheries for whitefish and trout in 1912 and 1915 so the total number of federal hatcheries in Ontario actually increased. Ontario also began a program of building hatcheries so that by 1925 it had seven hatcheries to the federal government's eight. Finally in 1926 the federal government transferred its hatcheries to the province.[12]

The transfer of responsibility for the administration and enforcement of fishery regulations from federal to provincial authorities did not involve sudden changes in the management of the fishery, but it did accelerate some existing tendencies. The result was a liberalization of regulations that by 1950 left the fishery "relatively unregulated."13

The basic principles of fishery management, first consolidated in the 1858 Fishery Act and incorporated in the 1868 federal Fisheries Act, were the encouragement of artificial propagation, the guarantee that fish would have access to their spawning grounds, the regulation of the time, methods, and place of fishing, the limitation of entry to the fishery by use of licences, and the control of pollution. As we have already seen, the provincial government continued the federal government's emphasis on the use of artificial propagation although the commercial benefits of the process were not proven. The province also continued to guarantee, through legislation, that fish would have access to their spawning grounds, but enforcement of this legislation was not much more effective than it had been under federal auspices.

The federal government had emphasized the importance of regulating the fishing season and had devoted much effort to enforcing close seasons. A close season during November (the spawning season) for whitefish and trout formed part of the first federal fishery regulations in 1868, and although there were serious exceptions in its enforcement, it continued to be a basic part of fishery management to the end of the century.

During the 1890s there was growing pressure on the federal government to suspend or abolish the close season. Fishermen argued that catches had been poor due to stormy weather or low fish stocks and that it was unfair to require Canadian fishermen to observe a close season when Americans did not. Although opposed by the professional staff of the Department of Marine and Fisheries, the arguments were increasingly successful after 1896.[14] In 1903 the close season on the Detroit River system and on most of Lake Erie was completely abandoned although the Ontario government protested that the change would ruin the fishery.[15] Twelve years later, when regulations were made in consultation with Ontario, the November close season for trout and whitefish was abandoned entirely on the Great Lakes where commercial fishing was permitted, although a close season was retained in sport-fishing areas. The close season on pickerel was abolished at the same time.[16] The concept of a close season was not totally abandoned; a prohibition of gill-net fishing on all or part of Lake Erie from 15 December to 15 March remained on the books until 1925, but the close season only covered the period when fishing was usually halted by ice and can have been of little practical value.

The only justification given for abandoning the close season was that artificial propagation made it unnecessary.[17] It may also have been a result of wartime demands for increased productivity and the declining influence of Professor Prince. Finally, there may have been a decision to place greater emphasis on preventing the capture of immature fish. There had been complaints for many years that vast numbers of immature fish were shipped to market or were simply thrown away. Small fish were not marketable, but competitive pressures made it difficult for dealers to resist purchasing them; one of the ostensible reasons for the formation of the fish trust was that it would reduce the number of small fish forced on the market.[18] In spite of the complaints, regulations establishing the minimum size of fish that could be kept were not introduced until 1907. These size limits only applied to bass, muskellunge, and pickerel; it was not until 1922 that size limits were placed on the major commercial species.[19]

Before 1907 the limitations on the size of mesh that could be used in various types of nets had been intended to limit the capture of immature fish: the federal 1868 Fisheries Act had established 5 inches extension measure as the standard for whitefish and lake trout nets.[20] Whether the regulations relating to net size were enforced with any consistency is doubtful. Testimony before the Dominion Fisheries Commission (1894) indicates that mesh size was a matter of individual choice.[21] Under the 1915 regulations, herring nets were to be 3 inches extension measure except in the eastern end of Lake Ontario and in Lake Superior where 2.5-inch mesh was permitted under certain circumstances. Trout and whitefish nets were to have 4.5-inch mesh. In broad terms these mesh sizes form the basis of today's regulations; however, it is unclear how consistently they have been enforced. For example, eastern Lake Erie fishermen used 2.75-inch mesh in 1915 and requested that they be allowed to continue using it because herring in the eastern end of the lake were smaller than in the western end. This was allowed on a temporary basis; subsequent extensions allowed the use of the undersize nets until at least 1921.[22]

The province also continued the federal government's policy of resisting radical technological innovations, such as the trap net and the bull net, that because of their efficiency would have greatly increased pressure on fish stocks. Neither government, however, restricted the powered net-lifter and nylon netting, both of which increased fishing intensity.

Although the Fishery Act of 1858 required that fishermen be licensed, no limit was put on the number of licences issued until the 1890s, when the federal government responded to concern about declining catches in areas such as the western end of Lake Erie by restricting the number of licences issued in threatened areas.[23] As a result the number of licensed fishermen fell during the 1890s. During the first two decades of provincial administration the number of licensed fishermen rose from about 2400 (1900) to 3200 (1920). In spite of the depressed state of the fishery during much of the 1930s and 1940s, the number of licensed fishermen remained above 2400 until the mid-1950s. Since the 1950s the government has resisted issuing new licences and has cancelled inactive licences.[24] Although the number of licensed fishermen on the lakes has been reduced to fewer than 1500, some authorities still contend that, given modern fishing methods, the number is too high.

The federal government also attempted to prevent excessive concentrations of fishing efforts by limiting gill-net licences to specific areas. Usually boats were licensed to fish in the vicinity of their home ports. The rule was not rigid and in some cases boats were licensed for more than one area. For example, many Goderich and Southampton fishermen held licences to fish in their own areas and off Manitoulin Island; however, when they attempted to acquire a third licence, to fish to the south of their home bases, they were refused.[25] After 1915 this rule was abandoned, at least on Lake Erie, and tugs were allowed to fish over the entire lake. As a result the entire fleet was able to concentrate in the areas of best fishing and greatly increase fishing intensity.[26] Pound-net fishermen were opposed to allowing gillnetters to fish the entire lake, and in 1937 they were able to convince the government to divide Lake Erie into eastern and western licence districts.[27] Today the lake is divided into three major licence zones and one minor zone, Long Point Bay. Most boats are only licensed to fish in one zone.[28]

Throughout the period when it had direct control of the fishery the federal government sought to preserve the fishery by limiting the catch through indirect means such as controlling times and places of fishing and preventing the use of gear that it considered too efficient. The provincial government has continued many of these practices and has also attempted to limit the catch by direct means, by imposing quotas. During World War I the provincial government charged a royalty of one quarter of a cent per pound on all annual catches over a certain amount. Although it was probably intended primarily as a wartime revenue measure, a side effect should have been to reduce the catch,[29] but the royalty was largely ineffective in reducing catches because the tax on excess catch was too low and because reporting catch size was voluntary. As a result of the second weakness, royalty payments fell from a high of $45 000 in 1924 to less than $10 000 in 1951.[30] In 1925 the Lake Erie Fishermen's Association and American associations on the south shore agreed to establish daily quotas of 6000 pounds per tug in order to maintain prices. This quota was subsequently included in Ontario regulations, but there is no evidence that it was enforced.[31] Perhaps, like so many other international Great Lakes fishery agreements of the 1920s and 1930s, it failed when one of the jurisdictions gave in to the pleas of its fishermen for special consideration. The concept of a quota re-emerged in the 1960s when a weekly catch limit of 20 tons was established for the Lake Erie smelt fishery. Although the official smelt quota has not been enforced by the government, the dominant smelt processor on the lake has successfully imposed a quota system on the fishermen.[32] More recently an international quota system has been established for walleye in western Lake Erie, and the Ontario government has established quotas for various fish in other lakes.

During the period of federal administration, pollution was largely a local problem that affected spawning areas and fisheries near large cities. As late as 1926 a survey stated that although there were serious local pollution problems on Lake Erie, the main body of the lake was relatively unpolluted.[33] By the late 1950s the situation had changed dramatically and it was widely reported that Lake Erie was dying. The principal problem was that various pollutants — sewage, phosphate-based soap, and agricultural fertilizer — were supporting rich growths of algae in the lake. When the algae died, its decay lowered the oxygen content of the deeper water and lowered the viability of the commercially desirable fish populations. The problem may have been exacerbated by an increase in the air temperature of one to two degrees Fahrenheit in the past 50 years, which has made the lake a less desirable habitat for cold-water fishes. In addition to natural increases in temperature, thermal pollution from water-cooled generating stations is a problem in certain localities.[34] The process of eutrophication has been partially reversed or at least slowed as a result of the Great Lakes Water Quality Agreement signed by Canada and the United States in 1972, but there is no practical solution to the problem of climatic change.

Toxic chemicals are an equally serious form of pollution. The dumping of toxic chemicals into waters inhabited by fish has been forbidden since 1857. In the nineteenth century the most serious polluters were tanneries and the early oil refineries, but they were relatively few and small. Moreover, they posed a danger to fish and not to consumers of fish. In the last 20 years governments have become aware that many toxic chemical pollutants such as mercury, PCBs, and myrex are concentrated in fish and pose direct threats to human health. As a result of mercury pollution the fishery on Lake St. Clair was closed completely in 1970, and other fisheries have been restricted at various times. The Great Lakes Water Quality Agreements of 1972 and 1978 were directed to solving this, as well as other pollution problems. To some extent they were successful: the Lake St. Clair fishery was reopened in 1980 and most of the fisheries in the upper lakes are open. There are, however, restrictions on lake trout, eels, carp, catfish, and mudpouts in Lake Ontario as a result of PCB and myrex contamination.[35]

International Jurisdiction

The international character of the Great Lakes has complicated fishery management in both the nineteenth and twentieth centuries. In addition to being under the jurisdiction of two nations, the lakes are within the jurisdiction of one province and eight states. In Canada from 1867 to 1899 the federal government was responsible for the fishery, but in the United States primary responsibility rested with the individual states. The American federal fisheries service has confined its activities to research, fish culture, and some international aspects of the fishery. State commissions have been responsible for the actual regulation. Divided jurisdiction may have resulted in less restrictive regulations on the American side of the border; Canadian fishermen frequently complained that they were being penalized by regulations, such as closed seasons, that Americans were not required to observe even though they shared the same fish stocks.[1] More recently, American fishermen have complained that they were subject to more stringent regulations than were Canadians.[2]

The problems posed by divided jurisdiction were recognized on both sides of the border at an early date and efforts were made to overcome them. Canadian and American officials were in contact with one another from the early 1870s, and between 1883 and 1936 there were at least 22 interstate and international conferences that attempted to establish a common fishery policy.[3] In 1892 Canada and the United States established an international fisheries commission to report on the prevention of overfishing and pollution, on the use of closed seasons, and on the restocking of fish in all border waters. In addition to making specific recommendations for managing the fishery in each of the Great Lakes, the commission recommended that a joint commission be established with power to regulate the entire fishery. It also recommended that uniform regulations be adopted for both the Canadian and American parts of each body of water and that the boundary on the Great Lakes be accurately established.[4]

Nothing came of these recommendations. The subject was considered again by the Joint High Commission of 1898–99, and a subcommittee prepared a draft treaty that was signed in 1908. The treaty provided for an international fisheries commission that could establish uniform fishing regulations for the Great Lakes. The regulations were to be implemented by the respective governments. A commission was appointed and regulations prepared, but the House of Representatives refused to approve them. As a result the treaty was abrogated in 1914.[5]

Some progress towards international control was made with the signing of the International Boundary Waters Treaty in 1909. Under the treaty an international joint commission was established to arbitrate questions concerning the use of international waters. Although its jurisdiction did not extend to the fishery, it did have authority to investigate sources of pollution of boundary waters.[6]

Following the collapse of the Lake Erie herring industry in 1925 a series of studies and conferences was instituted that led in 1933 to an agreement establishing common fishery regulations for Lake Erie. The agreement collapsed amidst mutual recriminations after only a season's operation.[7]

In 1940 Canada and the United States instituted another extensive inquiry into the Great Lakes fishery. In 1942 the board of inquiry recommended that, because the fishery was based on common stock, regulations should be established by a common agency. It also recommended that better statistics be kept and that tests be made of the effectiveness of planting fish. As a result of the recommendations a treaty was signed in 1946 that provided for an international commission to formulate common fishery regulations for the Great Lakes. Although local authorities were to be left with enforcement responsibilities, the commission was given power to take direct action if local authorities were ineffective. Both Wisconsin and Ohio objected to the treaty and it was never ratified.[8]

In the late 1940s a new predator, the sea lamprey, appeared in the Upper Great Lakes in large numbers. Its principal prey was the lake trout, a mainstay of the fishery in Lakes Huron, Superior, and Michigan. Following the appearance of the lamprey the catch of lake trout dropped dramatically. On Lake Huron the average catch in the 1930s was about 5 million pounds; by 1960 it had fallen to 1000 pounds. On Lake Superior the catch in the mid-1940s was about 4.5 million pounds; by 1960 it was under 500 000. A decline on a similar scale occurred on Lake Michigan. In response to the devastation caused by the sea lamprey, Canada and the United States established the Great Lakes Fishery Commission in 1954.[9] The commission was given power to organize fishery research and to implement a program to eradicate the lamprey. Although the commission has been unable to eliminate the lamprey, it has brought it under control and has prevented the disappearance of the lake trout although no major recovery has taken place. The commission has also undertaken research on other commercial fish, particularly the walleye in western Lake Erie.

In 1972 Canada and the United States took a further step towards protecting the fishery by signing the Great Lakes Water Quality Agreement. Essentially the agreement, since superseded by an agreement in 1978, provided specific direction and expanded the authority of the International Joint Commission to deal with pollution. The agreements provided for the control of both toxic substances and nutrient loading; the progress made in both areas since the signing of the agreement was noted in the previous chapter.

The relative positions of Canada and the United States in the Great Lakes fishery have changed substantially in the last three decades. The commercial fishery on the Great Lakes began in the United States, and throughout the nineteenth century over 80 per cent of the total catch on the lakes was taken from American waters although only about 64 per cent of the total area is within the United States. In addition, virtually all of the Canadian catch was exported to the United States. From 1900 to 1950 the Canadian fishery accounted for about 25 per cent of the total catch. During the 1950s the Canadian share of the catch began to increase rapidly, and since 1960 Canada has usually accounted for about 40 per cent of the total catch. Today the Canadian Lake Erie port of Wheatley claims to be the largest freshwater-fish-processing centre in the world. The rapid growth in the Canadian share of the catch is partially attributable to Canadian exploitation of smelt and yellow perch, but it is more directly attributable to the collapse of the American Lake Erie fishery. During the 1940s the Americans caught roughly two-thirds of the total catch on Lake Erie; today they catch about one-fifth of the total. The change is the result of several factors, only one of which is the depletion of American fish stocks. It is also due to a failure to innovate. Americans have not developed a smelt fishery although presumably smelt are as common in American waters as in Canadian. Labour productivity is higher in the Canadian fishery than it is in the American.[10] But perhaps the most important reason for the decline of American production is that a powerful sport-fishing lobby has limited the American commercial fishery.[11]

Commercial, Sport and Subsistence Fisheries

Competition among the different types of fisheries for finite resources has existed for as long as the different types of fisheries have existed, but it has grown more acute as fishing pressure has increased. Indian subsistence fisheries were established at most of the best inshore sites prior to European contact. Europeans established subsistence fisheries, which later evolved into commercial fisheries, on the same sites. A subsistence fishery involved a relatively low level of fishing effort and had no lasting effect on fish populations. Commercial fishing was much more intensive and in many cases severely reduced choice fish populations that had been the mainstay of the subsistence fishery. In 1884 Mr. O'Brien, the member of Parliament for Muskoka, reported that the inshore fishery, traditionally the resort of subsistence fishermen, was being destroyed and that fishermen had to go 20 to 30 miles from shore to catch fish.[1] Such voyages would have been beyond the capabilities of most subsistence fishermen. The depletion of the fishery by commercial fishermen led to regulations, such as the close season, that were applied to subsistence and commercial fishermen alike. In some cases the regulations probably made the subsistence fishery, which often depended on high concentrations of fish during the spawning season, impractical.

In some cases subsistence fishermen became commercial fishermen; in others, they were forced out of their locations or relegated to a minor status. According to traveller and artist George Catlin, the Ojibwa fishermen at Sault Ste. Marie were displaced by white commercial fishermen in the 1820s and 1830s; however, a recent historian of the fishery at the Sault has concluded that the Ojibwa remained active as commercial fishermen until the fishery failed in the 1880s.[2] On Manitoulin Island, particularly on the eastern end at Wikwemikong, the Ojibwa were involved in commercial fishing in the 1850s. They had adopted Mackinaw boats and were annually producing about 2000 barrels of salt fish that they traded to itinerant American merchants for fishing supplies and winter provisions.[3] The Ojibwa of the region believed that they had not surrendered their fishing rights under the Robinson Treaty of 1850 and contended that they should not be subject to fishery regulations. They received some support for this view from the superintendent general of Indian Affairs, but the Department of Marine and Fisheries refused to recognize their claims. When in 1875 the Noble brothers of Collingwood established a base on Squaw Island, which the Ojibwa regarded as their fishery, the department supported the Nobles. Over a period of years the Ojibwa were gradually restricted to a small fishing lease immediately adjoining their reservation.[4] Other Indian communities were restricted in a similar fashion, but in at least one case a traditional Indian fishery, the Fishing Islands of the Bruce Penninsula, was included in a reservation and was leased to commercial fishermen.[5]

Competition between commercial and sport fisheries on the Great Lakes did not become a serious problem until the twentieth century. In the nineteenth century sport fishermen were relatively few and there were apparently sufficient fish for everyone. Moreover, two mainstays of the commercial fishery, whitefish and herring, were not pursued by sport fishermen, who preferred bass, walleye, and brook trout. Potential conflict over lake trout stocks was largely defused by reserving most of the inland lakes, including Lake Nipigon prior to World War I, for sport fishing. Sport fishing was not prohibited on the Great Lakes, but it was expected to co-exist with commercial fishing. Because of the early importance of the tourism industry on the eastern shore of Georgian Bay, commercial fishing was limited in the inshore areas beginning in the 1890s; the limitation was also justified as providing a fish sanctuary.[6]

In southern Georgian Bay during the 1920s a charter-boat industry developed that competed with commercial fishermen for available trout stocks. Some commercial fishermen had been licensed to troll for trout rather than to net them and in the 1920s these fishermen began to charter their boats to sport fishermen. By the 1930s as many as 90 boats were involved in charters, but the industry failed with the disappearance of the trout in the 1940s. Although the co-existence of charter-boat and commercial fishing had potential for conflict, little is known of the relations between the two groups.[7]

In the United States, where sport fishermen were more numerous than in Canada and the safety valve of a large number of inland lakes was not available, restrictions on commercial fishing in favour of sport fishing appeared early in the twentieth century. Commercial fishing has been prohibited on the American waters of Lake St. Clair since 1909.[8] On the American side of Lake Erie, anglers obtained laws restricting the types of commercial fishing gear that could be used, and according to one authority, these regulations have been responsible for the technological stagnation of Ohio's fisheries.[9]

Sport fishing, as an element in the tourism industry, is a much more valuable industry than commercial fishing. As early as 1927 the game fishery in Ontario was estimated to be worth $82 million annually compared to $3.25 million for the commercial fishery.[10] More recently, the Great Lakes Fishery Commission estimated that as of 1979 the sport-fishing industry (tackle stores, marinas, restaurants, motels, gas stations, local government, etc.) on all of the Great Lakes was worth over $1 billion whereas the value of commercial fishing was estimated at $160 million.[11]

On the strength of the economic impact of sport fishing, and probably on the basis of voting strength, sport-fishing interests in the United States have been able to secure legislation that has restricted commercial fishing.[12] There has also been tension in Canada between sport and commercial fishermen; commercial fishermen have not, with minor exceptions, been permitted to take the salmon or splake that have been introduced to replace the lake trout. However, restrictions on Canadian commercial fishing have not been as severe as those imposed on the American commercial fishermen.

The Economic Impact
of the Great Lakes Fishery

Since its beginning the Great Lakes fishery has been the largest single component of the Canadian freshwater fishing industry. In the early years of the fishery, 1879–81, 93 per cent by value of Ontario fish were caught in the Great Lakes. Because of the method of reporting statistics it is impossible to do more than estimate the total value of Canada's freshwater fisheries in the nineteenth century, but there is little doubt that well over 50 per cent of all freshwater fish caught in Canada were caught in Ontario. Since the nineteenth century the changes in the types of fish caught in the Great Lakes and the development of other fisheries have reduced the relative value of the Great Lakes fishery, yet in spite of these changes the Great Lakes produced fish to an average value of $4 624 000 annually in the 1960s. This was equal to 80 per cent of the total catch for Ontario and 34 per cent of the total catch of freshwater fish in Canada.

In comparison with the other freshwater fisheries of Canada, the Great Lakes appear of predominant importance; in comparison with sea and inland fisheries combined, they appear less significant. In the years 1870–1900 the total landed value of Canadian fisheries (not including Newfoundland) averaged about $15.8 million dollars per year. Ontario's catch accounted for about $1.05 million, slightly ahead of that of Prince Edward Island ($1.04 million) but well behind that of Quebec ($1.9 million) and far behind Nova Scotia, New Brunswick, and British Columbia. Early in the twentieth century, Ontario replaced Quebec as the fourth most valuable fishery in Canada and held that position until the early 1960s, when it was superseded by Quebec and then by Prince Edward Island.

Although Ontario has the most important freshwater fishery in Canada, fishermen have never formed more than a miniscule part of the Ontario labour force. The first report of the Department of Marine and Fisheries, issued in 1868, stated that there were 1855 licensed fishermen in Ontario. In 1881 there were 2608, of whom 2296 were Great Lakes fishermen. In 1931 the number of Great Lakes licensed fishermen had increased to 2870 and by 1971 it had declined to 1306. The figures for licensed fishermen tend to exaggerate the true size of the labour force involved directly in fishing, for fishing was a seasonal and part-time activity. Many fishermen, particularly in the nineteenth century, were also farmers, lumbermen, and labourers. The 1881 census lists only 766 individuals who were primarily engaged in fishing in Ontario compared to the 2608 who were licensed to fish. In 1931 there were 2772 full-time fishermen and 2870 licensed fishermen; in 1971 the comparable figures are 905 and 1306. In addition to the actual fishermen there were, and are, workers in fishery service industries — packing, shipping, selling, and boatbuilding — nevertheless it is safe to say that the fishery has never employed more than 0.5 per cent of Ontario's labour force. The proportion of actual fishermen in the Ontario labour force has consistently been lower than that of any province with the exceptions of Alberta and Saskatchewan (*see* Appendix, Table 5).

Finally, in considering the effect of the fishing industry on life in Ontario, it must be remembered that the fishing population, small to begin with, has been scattered along the shores of the Great Lakes. Only rarely have as many as 50 licensed fishermen operated out of the same port. Moreover, fishermen were mobile and frequently shifted their bases of operation as fish stocks rose and fell. For example, the Lake Erie fishery began in the western end of the lake; during the years of the great herring fishery before and during the First World War, the focus of the fishery shifted to the eastern end of the lake; it has now shifted back to the western end. Some of the most important early fisheries are now insignificant, most notably the inshore fisheries near Toronto and Hamilton, and those on Lake St. Clair and the Detroit River. The fishing industry in the vicinity of Manitoulin Island is also greatly reduced from its former importance. On the other hand, fisheries in the Prince Edward County area and on Lake Erie (particularly at its western end) are relatively as important as they were a century ago.

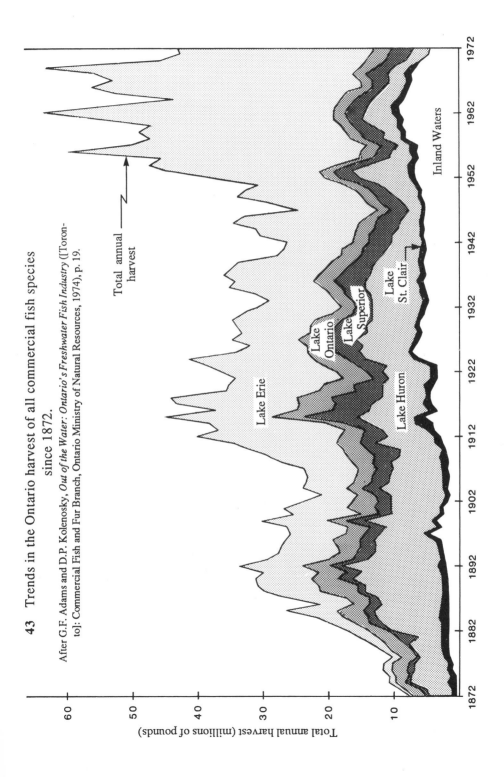

43 Trends in the Ontario harvest of all commercial fish species since 1872.

After G.F. Adams and D.P. Kolenosky, *Out of the Water: Ontario's Freshwater Fish Industry* ([Toronto]: Commercial Fish and Fur Branch, Ontario Ministry of Natural Resources, 1974), p. 19.

Appendix
Statistical Tables

Table 1
**Three-Year-Average Catches of All Fish in Canadian Waters
of the Great Lakes (Thousands of Pounds)**

	Ontario	Erie	St. Clair	Huron	Superior	Total
1869–71	1586	569	466	3477	621	6719
1879–81	3035	2235	983	5136	561	11 950
1889–91	4435	8787	899	12 710	2133	28 964
1899–1901	3134	10 090	708	8451	2461	24 844
1909–11	3830	14 480	767	6930	4080	30 087
1919–21	5023	15 783	1256	6460	3437	31 959
1929–31	3500	12 582	506	7210	4262	28 060
1939–41	3202	10 993	891	5843	3354	24 283
1949–51	2212	16 368	468	4626	2898	26 572
1959–61	2039	32 171	793	3907	3010	41 920
1969–71	2694	36 294	*	2404	3233	44 625
1979–81	2162	43 017	142	3778	4303	53 402

* The Lake St. Clair Fishery was closed from 1970 to 1980.

Sources
1869–1971: Norman S. Baldwin et al., *Commercial Fish Production in the Great Lakes, 1867–1977* (Ann Arbor: Great Lakes Fishery Commission, 1979).
1979–81: Ontario. Ministry of Natural Resources, *Statistics, 1982...* [Toronto: 1982].

Table 2
**Three-Year-Average Dollar Value of Catches of All Fish in the
Canadian Waters of the Great Lakes (Thousands of Dollars)**

	Ontario	Erie	St. Clair	Huron	Superior	Total
1871	$ 60	$ 12	$ 22	$ 91	$ 16	$ 201
1879–81	113	54	33	184	26	410
1889–91	243	422	48	943	168	1824
1899–1901	108	312	34	651	221	1326
1907–10	247	689	66	661	235	1898
1919, 1921	397	907	60	581	461	2406
1929–31	264	749	32	709	354	2108
1939–41	206	738	47	556	273	1820
1949–51	330	2997	60	1291	609	5287
1959–61	381	2256	139	1022	287	4085
1969–71	402	4090	188*	817	427	5924
1979–81	1254	13 833	23**	2827	1879	19 816

* 1969–70
** 1981

Sources
1870–1910: Canada. Dept. of Marine and Fisheries, *Annual Report ... 1870* to ... *1883* (Ottawa: imprint varies, 1871–84).
Canada. Dept. of Fisheries, *Annual Report ... 1884* to ... *1891* (Ottawa: imprint varies, 1885–92).
Canada. Dept. of Marine and Fisheries. *Annual Report ... 1892* to ... *1910–11* (Ottawa: imprint varies, 1893–1911).
1920–50: Ontario. Game and Fisheries Branch/Dept., *Annual Report ... 1920* to ... *1945/46* (Toronto: imprint varies, 1921–46).
(Ontario. Dept. of Lands and Forests, *Annual Report ... 1947* to ... *1950* (Toronto: imprint varies, 1948–51).
1960–70: Canada. Dept. of Trade and Commerce. Dominion Bureau of Statistics, *Fisheries Statistics...* (Ottawa: title and imprint vary, 1961–64).
Canada. Dominion Bureau of Statistics, *Fisheries Statistics...* (Ottawa: title and imprint vary, 1965–70).
Canada. Statistics Canada, *Fisheries Statistics of Canada: Canada Summary* (Ottawa: Information Canada, 1971).
1980: Ontario. Ministry of Natural Resources, *Statistics, 1982...* [Toronto: 1982].

Table 3
Three-Year-Averages of Numbers of Licensed Fishermen on Canadian Great Lakes

	Ontario	Erie	St. Clair	Huron	Superior	Total
1871	625	202	31	620	146	1906
1879–81	808	204	316	620	131	2079
1889–91	684	496	334	1193	147	2854
1899–1901	546	500	222	936	238	2442
1907–10	656	769	335	948	153	2861
1919–21	994	902	268	776	332	3272
1929–31	714	794	146	1003	347	3004
1939–41	576	887	129	937	380	2909
1949–51	649	1057	705	12	327	2615
1959–61	486	790	86	347	194	1903
1969–71	258	530	56*	253	129	1226
1979–81	328	652	10**	308	177	1475

* 1969–70
** 1981

Sources
1870–1910: Canada. Dept. of Marine and Fisheries, *Annual Report ... 1870 to ... 1883* (Ottawa: imprint varies, 1871–84).
Canada. Dept of Fisheries, *Annual Report ... 1884* to .. *1891* (Ottawa: imprint varies, 1885–92).
Canada. Dept. of Marine and Fisheries, *Annual Report ... 1892* to ... *1910–11* (Ottawa: imprint varies, 1893–1911).
1920–70: Canada. Dept. of Trade and Commerce. Dominion Bureau of Statistics, *Fisheries Statistics...* (Ottawa: title and imprint vary, 1921–64).
Canada. Dominion Bureau of Statistics, *Fisheries Statistics...* (Ottawa: title and imprint vary, 1965–70).
Canada. Statistics Canada, *Fisheries Statistics of Canada: Canada Summary* (Ottawa: Information Canada, 1971).
1980: Ontario. Ministry of Natural Resources, *Statistics, 1982...* [Toronto: 1982].

Table 4
Average Value of Fish Caught in Canada by Decade* (Thousands of Dollars)

	Nfld.	N.S.	P.E.I.	N.B.	Que.	Ont.
1870–79	—	$ 5738	$ 614	$ 2063	$ 1832	$ 351
1880–89	—	7533	1308	3354	2016	1205
1890–99	—	6789	1073	3868	1973	1672
1900–09	—	7806	1141	4522	2010	1701
1910–19	—	10 694	1302	5035	2664	2796
1920–29	—	10 657	1402	4820	2570	3418
1930–39	—	5046	695	1944	1784	2354
1940–49	—	14 198	1766	5204	3325	4632
1950–59	$13 551	23 422	3209	7460	3694	6863
1960–69	23 075	42 273	6333	11 042	6837	5853
1970–79	67 383	109 347	14 917	28 750	18 482	12 278

* Market value to 1929; landed value from 1930.
** Includes Saskatchewan, Alberta, and the Yukon to 1920–29.

Sources
1870–1929: Canada. Dept. of Trade and Commerce. Dominion Bureau of Statistics. Fisheries Statistics Branch, *Fisheries Statistics of Canada, 1931* (Ottawa: F.A. Acland, 1932), p. 53.
1930–59: M.C. Urquhart and K.A.H. Buckley, *Historical Statistics of Canada* (Toronto: Macmillan, 1965), Series M1-11.
1960–79: *Annual Statistical Review of Canadian Fisheries*, Vols. 1–12 (1969–80).

Table 4
(Continued)

Man.**	Sask.	Alta.	Yukon & NWT	B.C.	Canada
$ —	$ —	$ —	$ —	$ 561	$ 10 637
166	—	—	—	1689	17 173
685	—	—	—	4138	20 199
1258	—	—	—	6783	25 221
1575	—	—	—	16 598	40 664
2604	—	—	—	22 035	47 507
1092	172	180	—	7712	20 993
2919	580	400	—	20 112	53 288
3439	837	719	—	35 301	96 449
3766	1530	836	831	46 930	149 320
7707	$2247	$577	$1051	$139 960	$401 050

Table 5
Fishermen* as a Percentage of the
Labour Force in Each Province and in Canada
1881, 1931, and 1971

	1881	1931	1971
Canada	1.6 %	0.9 %	0.3 %
Newfoundland			4.8
Nova Scotia	9.6	6.3	2.2
Prince Edward Island	2.3	4.5	4.8
New Brunswick	1.7	3.0	1.1
Quebec	0.9	0.4	0.07
Ontario	0.1	0.2	0.03
Manitoba	0.2	0.6	0.06
Saskatchewan	1.1	0.05	0.06
Alberta		0.01	0.02
British Columbia	10.3	2.5	0.4
Yukon & N.W.T			0.4

* Persons whose principal occupation was fishing.

Sources

Canada. Ministry of Agriculture, *Census of Canada, 1880–81/Recensement du Canada* (Ottawa: MacLean, Roger & Co., 1882–85), Vol. 2, Table 14.
Canada. Dept. of Trade and Commerce. Dominion Bureau of Statistics, *Seventh Census of Canada, 1931* (Ottawa: J.O. Patenaude, Kings Printer, 1933–42), Vol. 7, Table 58.
Canada. Statistics Canada, *1971 Census of Canada, Volume Series* (Ottawa: 1972–77), Vol. 3, Pt. 2, Catalogue No. 94-717, Classifications 7311, 7313.

List of Abbreviations

CCI   Canada. Commission of Inquiry into Freshwater Fish Marketing.

CDFC   Canada. Dominion Fishery Commission.

CF   Canada. Department of Fisheries.

CGB   Canada. Georgian Bay Fisheries Commission.

CMF   Canada. Department of Marine and Fisheries.

CNSFB   Canada. Department of the Naval Service. Fisheries Branch.

CPCL   Canada (Province). Department of Crown Lands.

CPHC   Canada. Parliament. House of Commons.

CPLA   Canada (Province). Legislative Assembly.

JFC   Joint Fisheries Commission (U.S. and Great Britain)

NA   Canada. National Archives.

OA   Ontario. Archives.

OF   Ontario. Department of Fisheries.

OGF   Ontario. Game and Fisheries Branch/Department.

OLF   Ontario. Department of Lands and Forests.

ONR   Ontario. Ministry of Natural Resources.

USTC   United States. Tarriff Commission.

Endnotes

Introduction

1 Statistics regarding catch, manpower, and gear used on the Great Lakes are taken from the sources named in Tables 1 to 5.

Background

1 Tom H. Whillans, "Fish Community Transformation in Three Bays within the Lower Great Lakes" (MA thesis, Dept. of Geography, Univ. of Toronto, Toronto, 1977) (hereafter cited as "Fish Community"), pp. 31–35.

2 Graham Alexander Macdonald, "The Saulteur-Ojibwa Fishery at Sault Ste. Marie, 1640–1920" (MA thesis, Univ. of Waterloo, Waterloo, Ont., 1978) (hereafter cited as "Saulteur-Ojibwa Fishery"), p. 35.

3 Canada (Province). Board of Registration and Statistics, *Appendix to the First [Census] Report* (Montreal: Stewart Derbishire and George Desbarats, Queen's Printers, 1849), p. 8; ibid., *Census of the Canadas, 1851–52* (Quebec: Printed by John Lovell, 1853–55) (hereafter cited as *Census of the Canadas, 1851–52*), Vol. 1, p. 36.

4 T.H. Whillans, "Fish Community," p. 186; Stephen Kendall, J.R. Payne, and William F. Sinclair, "Lake Erie Fisheries Management Plan," Ontario Ministry of Natural Resources, [Toronto], 1977 (hereafter cited as "Lake Erie Fisheries", p. 3.

5 "The United States Fresh Water Fishery Then and Now," *The Great Lakes Fisherman*, Vol. 3, No. 8 (June 1976), p. 13; Harlan H. Hatcher, *The Great Lakes* (London: Oxford Univ. Press, 1944), p. 287; JFC, *Report of the Joint Commission Relative to the Preservation of the Fisheries in Waters Contiguous to Canada and the United States* (Ottawa: S.E. Dawson, Queen's Printer, 1897) (hereafter cited as *Report of the Joint Commission*), pp. 72–73.

6 T.H. Whillans, "Fish Community," p. 185.

7 I.M. Wellington and C.C. James, "Presqu'isle," *Ontario Historical Society, Papers and Records*, Vol. 5 (1904) (hereafter cited as "Presqu'isle"), p. 72.

8 Ronald Tiessen, "The Delaurier House — Family Study, Point Pelee," MS on file, Environment Canada, Canadian Parks Service, Ontario Regional Office, Cornwall, 1979, "Economic Activities," n.p.

9 Milo M. Quaife, ed., *The John Askin Papers* (Detroit: Detroit Library Commission, 1928–31) (hereafter cited as *John Askin Papers*), Vol. 2, pp. 574, 583.

10   John Jeremiah Bigsby, *The Shoe and the Canoe...* (London: Chapman and Hall, 1850), Vol. 2, pp. 122, 125.

11   Frederick Marryat, *A Diary in America, with Remarks on its Institutions* (Philadelphia: Carey and Hart, 1839), p. 98.

12   William Sherwood Fox, *The Bruce Beckons; The Story of Lake Huron's Great Peninsula* (Toronto: Univ. of Toronto Press, 1952) (hereafter cited as *The Bruce*), pp. 109–113.

13   Victor Lauriston, *Lambton's Hundred Years, 1849–1949* (Sarnia, Ont.: Haines Frontier Print Co., 1949), pp. 105-06; James P. Barry, *Georgian Bay; The Sixth Great Lake* (Toronto: Clarke Irwin, 1968), pp. 105-11.

14   Grace Lee Nute, "The American Fur Company's Fishing Enterprises on Lake Superior," *Mississippi Valley Historical Review*, Vol. 12, No. 4 (March 1926) (hereafter cited as "American Fur Company"), pp. 483–503; United States. Treasury Dept., *Communication from the Secretary of the Treasury, Transmitting ... the Report ... on the Trade and Commerce of the British North American Colonies and Upon the Trade of the Great Lakes and Rivers...* (Washington, D.C.: R. Armstrong, Printer, 1853), p. 209.

15   Susan Campbell, *Fort William: Living and Working at the Post* (Fort William Archaeological Project, Ontario Ministry of Culture and Recreation, Toronto, 1976), pp. 68–69.

16   John M. Weiler, "Michipicoten: Hudson's Bay Company Post, 1821–1904," in *Three Heritage Studies on the History of the HBC Michipicoten Post and on the Archeology of the North Pickering Area*, ed. David Skene Melvin (Toronto: Historical Planning and Research Branch, Ontario Ministry of Culture and Recreation, 1980), p. 29; NA, MG20, B.194/b/10, p. 13, Mourse to Bethune, 17 July 1835, and D.4/104, p. 7, minutes of the council of the Southern Department, 23 May 1836.

17   Canada (Province). Board of Registration and Statistics, *Census of the Canadas, 1851–52*, Vol. 2, p. 65.

18   CPCL, "First Report of the Superintendent of Fisheries for Upper Canada" in *Report of the Commissioner of Crown Lands of Canada for the Year 1857* (Toronto: John Lovell, 1858) (hereafter cited as *Crown Lands ... 1857*), pp. 90–91. The value of the fisheries has been converted from pounds currency to dollars at the rate of $4 per £1 currency.

19   William Sherwood Fox, "The Literature of the Salmo Salar in Lake Ontario and Tributary Streams," *Proceedings and Transactions of the Royal Society of Canada*, 3rd ser., Vol. 24, Sect. 2 (1930), p. 50; CPCL, *Crown Lands ... 1857*, pp. 81, 87.

Pre-Confederation
Legislation and Regulations

1   Upper Canada, *Statutes* (imprint varies, 1807–40) (hereafter cited as *Statutes*), 47 Geo. III, c. 12, 1807; ibid., 50 Geo. III, c. 3, 1810.

2   Ibid., 9 Geo. IV, c. 4, 1828.

3   John Richardson Dymond, "The Fisheries of the Great Lakes," in J.R. Dymond, ed., *Fish and Wildlife: A Memorial to W.J.R. Harkness* (Toronto: Longman's, 1964) (hereafter cited as "Fisheries of the Great Lakes"), p. 86.

4   Upper Canada, *Statutes*, 4 Geo. IV, c. 37, 1823; ibid., 6 Will. IV, c. 15, 1836; ibid., 3 Will. IV, c. 29, 1833; Canada (Province). Parliament, *Statutes...* (imprint varies, 1841–58) (hereafter cited as *Statutes*), 7 Vict., c. 13, 1843.

5   Canada (Province). Parliament, *Statutes*, 3 Vict., c. 24, 1840.

6   Ibid., 20 Vict., c. 21, 1857; ibid., 22 Vict., c. 86, 1858.

7   NA, RG1, E1, Vol. 64, p. 628, 23 Oct. 1845 (reel C-111).

8 Upper Canada, *Statutes*, 2 Vict., c. 16, 1839; Canada (Province). Parliament, *Statutes*, 7 Vict., c. 16, 1843, and 10–11 Vict., c. 20, 1847.

9 Canada. Laws and Statutes, etc., *Statutes of Canada...* (Ottawa: Malcolm Cameron, Queen's Printer, 1868) (hereafter cited as *Statutes*), 31 Vict., c. 60, s. 14.2, 1868.

10 CPCL, *Crown Lands ... 1866*, p. 52.

11 Ibid., *1859*, p. 80; NA, RG1, E1, Vol. 88, pp. 149, 259, 297–98 (reel C-121); Richard Stanton Lambert and Paul Pross, *Renewing Nature's Wealth...* ([Toronto]: Ontario Dept. of Lands and Forests, 1967) (hereafter cited as *Renewing Nature's Wealth*), pp. 153–54.

Technological Development
Fishing Gear

1 Donald Wayne Lewis, *The Decline of the Lake Erie Commercial Fishing Industry in Ohio* (Ann Arbor: University Microfilms International, 1982) (hereafter cited as *Lake Erie Commercial Fishing*), p. 124.

2 Nets are generally measured diagonally from one knot to the opposite knot with the net stretched taut. A 2-inch extension measure net forms a square with 1-inch sides. Canada (Province). Parliament, *Statutes*, 22 Vict. c. 68, s. 30, 1858; CDFC, *Report of the Dominion Fishery Commission on the Fisheries of the Province of Ontario, 1893*, Samuel Wilmot and Edward Harris (Ottawa: S.E. Dawson, Queen's Printer, 1894) (hereafter cited as *Dominion Fisheries Commission ... Ontario*), Pt. 1, pp. 51, 57.

3 CDFC, *Dominion Fisheries Commission ... Ontario*, Pt. 1, pp. 51–54, 56–57.

4 William Henry Giles Kingston, *Western Wanderings; or, A Pleasure Tour in the Canadas* (London: Chapman and Hall, 1856), Vol. 1, p. 222; G.A. Macdonald, "Saulteur-Ojibwa Fishery," pp. 65–66, 79–80.

5 CDFC, *Dominion Fisheries Commission ... Ontario*, Pt. 1, pp. 311–5.

6 Ralph Hile, Paul H. Eschmeyer, and George F. Lunger, "Status of the Lake Trout Fishery in Lake Superior," *Transactions of the American Fisheries Society*, Vol. 80 (1950), pp. 299–300; F.T. Tomkins, *The Life History and Reproduction of Georgian Bay Lake Trout, with Some Notes on the Commercial Fishery* (MA thesis, Univ. of Toronto, Toronto, 1951), pp. 59–61; David H. Loftus, *The Charterboat Fishery for Lake Trout in Southern Georgian Bay: 1920–1955* (n.p.: Lake Huron Fisheries Assessment Unit, Ontario Ministry of Natural Resources, 1979) (hereafter cited as *Charterboat Fishery*).

7 CDFC, *Dominion Fisheries Commission ... Ontario*, Pt. 1, pp. 227–29.

8 CPHC, *Official Report of the Debates of the House of Commons...* (Ottawa: Queen's Printer, 1884–94) (hereafter cited as *Debates*), 6 April 1894, p. 843, and 9 April 1894, p. 951.

9 NA, RG23, Vol. 105, File 94, p. 12, 8 Jan. 1844 (reel T-2718).

10 Joan Lenore Ellsworth, "The Eastern Lake Ontario Commercial Fishery, 1673–190: A Cultural Heritage, A Forgotten Staple" (MA thesis, Queen's Univ., Kingston, 1983), p. 87; John Van Oosten, "Michigan's Commercial Fisheries of the Great Lakes," *Michigan History Magazine*, Vol. 22, No. 1 (Winter 1938), p. 13; JFC, *Report of the Joint Commission*, p. 60; William A. Kennedy, *Daily Catch Record of the Crewe Brothers Fishery, Lake Erie, 1904 to 1956* (London, Ont.: Fisheries Research Board of Canada, 1961) (hereafter cited as *Daily Catch Record*), Vol. 1, p. 27.

11 CMF, *Annual Report ... 1880* to *... 1883* (Ottawa: imprint varies, 1881–84) (hereafter cited as *Annual Report...*), statistical reports; CF, *Annual Report ... 1884* to *... 1885* (Ottawa: imprint varies, 1885–86) (hereafter cited as *Annual Report...*), statistical reports.

12   CDFC, *Dominion Fisheries Commission ... Ontario*, Pt. 1, p. 207; NA, RG2, 1, Vol. 537, order-in-council 2461, 11 Dec. 1899.

13   JFC, *Report of the Joint Commission*, pp. 120–21.

14   Canada, *Ontario Fishery Regulations and Amendments to March 1, 1980* ([Toronto]: Ontario Ministry of Natural Resources, [1980]), p. 113.

15   James Cleland Hamilton, *The Georgian Bay; An Account of its Position, Inhabitants, Mineral Interests, Fish, Timber and Other Resources...* (Toronto: Carswell Co., 1893), pp. 105–06; CGB, *Report and Recommendations (with Appendices) of the Dominion Fisheries Commission Appointed to Enquire into the Fisheries of Georgian Bay and Adjacent Waters, 1905–1908*, John Birnie, James J. Noble, and E.E. Prince (Ottawa: Govt. Printing Bureau, 1908) (hereafter cited as *Dominion Fisheries Commission ... Georgian Bay*), p. 7.

16   T.H. Whillans, "Fish Community," pp. 31–32; I.M. Wellington and C.C. James, "Presqu'isle," pp. 71–72.

17   JFC, *Report of the Joint Commission*, pp. 103–15.

18   G.L. Nute, "American Fur Company," p. 492.

19   CMF, *Annual Report ... 1868* to ... *1883*, statistical returns; CF, *Annual Report ... 1884* to ... *1891*, statistical returns; CMF, *Annual Report ... 1892* to ... *1913–14*, statistical returns; CNSFB, *Annual Report ... 1914–15* to ... *1916–17* (Ottawa: imprint varies, 1915–17) (hereafter cited as *Annual Report...*), statistical returns. As late as 1922 the investment in pound nets on Lake Erie was $727 500 compared to $165 734 invested in gill nets. (OGF, *Annual Report ... 1922*, pp. 40–1.) Investment in gill nets used on Lake Erie did not exceed investment in pound nets until 1941 (CF, *Annual Report ... 1940–41* (Ottawa: Edward Cloutier, King's Printer, 1941), fisheries statistics, pp. 170–71.) In 1953 R.G. Ferguson reported that pound nets were still more abundant than gill nets in the central basin of Lake Erie (R.G. Ferguson, *Lake Erie Commercial Fisheries: A Preliminary Appraisal* ([Toronto]: Ontario Dept. of Lands and Forests, 1955) (hereafter cited as *Lake Erie Commercial Fisheries*), pp. 2–3.

20   CF, *Annual Report ... 1890*, pp. xlix–l; R.G. Ferguson, *Lake Erie Commercial Fisheries*.

21   CF, *Annual Report ... 1890*, pp. xliv–l and App. 6; CGB, *Dominion Fisheries Commission ... Georgian Bay*, p. 17; NA, RG23, Vol. 157, File 466, pp. 35–42, 9 Jan. 1894, and Vol. 128, File 179, Smith to Davies, 24 Feb. 1897.

22   JFC, *Report of the Joint Commission*, pp. 40, 71, 115; CGB, *Dominion Fisheries Commission ... Georgian Bay*, pp. 8, 19–20; John Peters, "Commercial Fishing in Lake Huron, 1880–1915: The Exploitation and Decline of the Whitefish and Lake Trout" (MA thesis, Dept. of Geography, Univ. of Western Ontario, London, Ont., 1981) (hereafter cited as "Commercial Fishing in Lake Huron"), p. 107; William A. Kennedy, *A History of Commercial Fishing in Inland Canada* (London, Ont.: Fisheries Research Board of Canada, n.d.) (hereafter cited as *History of Commercial Fishing*), p. 29.

23   United States. Tariff Commission, *Lake Fish: A Study of the Trade Between the United States and Canada in Fresh-Water Fish with Cost of Production Data* (Washington, D.C.: USGPO, 1927) (hereafter cited as *Lake Fish*), p. 93; Walter N. Koelz, "Fishing Industry of the Great Lakes," in United States. Bureau of Fisheries, *Report of the United States Commissioner of Fisheries for the Fiscal Year 1925* (Washington, D.C.: USGPO, 1926), App. 11 (hereafter cited as "Fishing Industry"), pp. 558–59; Henry A. Regier and W.L. Hartman, "Lake Erie's Fish Community: 150 Years of Cultural Stresses," *Science*,

Vol. 180, No. 4092 (22 June 1973) (hereafter cited as "Lake Erie's Fishing Community"), pp. 1251.

24   NA, RG23, Vol. 927, File 721-4-5 [7 and 8], Anderson et al. to minister, 22 Jan. 1922; Canada, *The Canada Gazette*, 25 July 1925, p. 243, Special Fishing Regulations for the Province of Ontario, Section 13c.

25   W.N. Koelz, "Fishing Industry," pp. 558–59.

26   CCI, *Report...*, George H. McIvor (Ottawa: Queen's Printer, [1966]) (hereafter cited as *Report*), pp. 19–29; Donald K. Tressler and James M. Lemon et al., *Marine Products of Commerce...* (New York: Book Division, Reinhold, 1951) (hereafter cited as *Marine Products of Commerce*), pp. 242, 234; George Browne Goode et al., "History and Methods of the Fisheries," in G.B. Goode et al., *The Fisheries and Fishery Industries of the United States...* (Washington, D.C.: USGPO, 1884–87), Pt. 5 (hereafter cited as "History and Methods of the Fisheries"), p. 764; USTC, *Report to the United States Senate on Nets and Netting and Other Fishing Gear...* (Washington, D.C.: USGPO, 1937), pp. 6–7. I am indebted to W. Jack Christie, Great Lakes Coordinator, Ontario Ministry of Natural Resources, for the information on the survival of linen nets on Lake Ontario.

27   W.A. Kennedy, *History of Commercial Fishing*, p. 29.

28   H.C. Mersereau, "Some Aspects of the Use of Nylon Fishing Gear," [*Proceedings of the*] *Ninth Annual Meeting, Fisheries Council of Canada, April 26–28, 1954 ... Ottawa* (Ottawa: Fisheries Council of Canada, n.d.), pp. 25–27; W.J. Christie, *A Study of Freshwater Fishery Regulations Based on North American Experience* (Rome: Food and Agriculture Organization of the United Nations, 1978) (hereafter cited as *North American Experience*), pp. 22–24.

29   Hugh M. Smith and Merwin-Marie Snell, comp., "[Review of the] Fisheries of the Great Lakes in 1885...," in United States. Commission of Fish and Fisheries, *Report of the Commissioner for 1887* (Washington, D.C.: USGPO, 1891) App. 1 (hereafter cited as "Fisheries of the Great Lakes in 1885"), p. 75; CCI, *Report*, pp. 19–29.

30   John Jacob Van West, "The Independent Fishermen in the Port Dover Fishing Industry: A Case Study of Their Production and Market Relations," (PhD thesis, Univ. of Toronto, Toronto, 1983) (hereafter cited as "Independent Fishermen"), pp. 28–30, 47–49, 152–53; pers. com., W.J. Christie.

Technological Development: Boats

1   G.B. Goode, "History and Methods of the Fisheries," p. 759; H.M. Smith and M.-M. Snell, comp., "Fisheries of the Great Lakes in 1885," Pl. 6, pp. 26–28.

2   W.A. Kennedy, *History of Commercial Fishing*, p. 29.

3   H.M. Smith and M.-M. Snell, comp., "Fisheries of the Great Lakes in 1885," pp. 28–29; G.B. Goode, "History and Methods of the Fisheries," p. 760; CDFC, *Dominion Fisheries Commission ... Ontario*, Pt. 2, p. 112.

4   H.M. Smith and M.-M. Snell, comp., "Fisheries of the Great Lakes in 1885," pp. 22–24.

5   James W. Milner, "Report on the Fisheries of the Great Lakes: The Result of Inquiries Prosecuted in 1871 and 1872," in United States. Commission of Fish and Fisheries, *Report of the Commissioner for 1872 and 1873* (Washington, D.C.: USGPO, 1874), Pt. 2, App. A (hereafter cited as "Fisheries of the Great Lakes"), pp. 11–14; Howard Irving Chapelle, *American Small Sailing Craft: Their Design, Development, and Construction* (New York: W.W. Norton and Co., 1951), pp. 180–85; W.S. Fox, *The Bruce*, p. 119.

6 H.M. Smith and M.-M. Snell, comp., "Fisheries of the Great Lakes in 1885," p. 19; Frank Prothero, *The Good Years: A History of the Commercial Fishing Industry on Lake Erie* (Belleville: Mika Publishing, 1973) (hereafter cited as *The Good Years*), p. 91.

7 H.M. Smith and M.-M. Snell, comp., "Fisheries of the Great Lakes in 1885," pp. 19–21, 220.

8 G.C. Toner, "The Great Lakes Fisheries: Unheeded Depletion," *Canadian Forum*, Vol. 19, No. 224 (Sept. 1939), p. 178.

9 W.A. Kennedy, *History of Commercial Fishing*, p. 29; "Death Claims Edward Crossley, Inventor of the Original Crossley Net Lifter," *The Fisherman*, Vol. 15, No. 5 (May 1947), p. 18; J. Peters, "Commercial Fishing in Lake Huron," p. 110.

10 NA, RG23, Vol. 139, File 317, Post to Gordon, 27 Feb. 1905.

11 F. Prothero, *The Good Years*, pp. 91–92, 96.

12 Ibid., pp. 32–33, 97.

13 CCI, *Report*, pp. 21–23.

14 Thomas E. Colvin, "Main-Stay of the Great Lakes," *The Canadian Fisherman*, Vol. 46, No. 11 (Nov. 1959), pp. 38–39.

15 J.J. Van West, "Independent Fishermen," pp. 55–56.

16 F. Prothero, *The Good Years*, pp. 97–99; *see also* all issues of *The Great Lakes Fisherman*.

Technological Development
Processing and Distribution

1 M.M. Quaife, ed., *John Askin Papers*, Vol. 2, p. 583; D.W. Lewis, *Lake Erie Commercial Fishing*, p. 26.

2 G.L. Nute, "American Fur Company," p. 500.

3 Charles W. Triggs, "The Problem of Getting our Fish to the Customer. Distribution," *Fishing Gazette*, Vol. 52, No. 7, Annual Review Number (1935), pp. 100, 103; H.M. Smith and M.-M. Snell, comp., "Fisheries of the Great Lakes in 1885," pp. 211, 264.

4 CPCL, *Crown Lands ... 1859*, App. 31.

5 CF, *Annual Report ... 1885*, p. 317; statistical reports in CMF, *Annual Report ... 1868* to ... *1883*, CF, *Annual Report ... 1884* to ... *1891*, and CMF, *Annual Report ... 1892* to ... *1900*; USTC, *Lake Fish*, p. 123.

6 Maurice Earl Stansby, *Industrial Fishery Technology; A Survey of Methods for Domestic Harvesting, Preservation, and Processing of Fish Used for Food and for Industrial Products* (New York: Reinhold, 1963) (hereafter cited as *Industrial Fishing Technology*), p. 283.

7 H.M. Smith and M.-M. Snell, comp., "Fisheries of the Great Lakes in 1885," p. 26.

8 CMF, *Annual Report ... 1879*, p. 323; CDFC, *Dominion Fisheries Commission ... Ontario*, Pt. 1, pp. 221–26.

9 NA, RG33, No. 79, Vol. 6, p. 832, Omstead testimony.

10 M. Stansby, *Industrial Fishing Technology*, p. 283; USTC, *Lake Fish*, p. 113.

11 D.K. Tressler and J.M. Lemon et al., *Marine Products of Commerce*, pp. 347–49.

12 "The Package Fish Trade in the U.S.," *The Canadian Fisherman*, Vol. 15, No. 8 (Aug. 1928); "History of Filleting," *The Canadian Fisherman*, Vol. 16 (Aug. 1929), p. 34.

13 J.N. Lewis, "The Fish Stick Story," in *[Proceedings of the] Tenth Annual Meeting, Fisheries Council of Canada, April 18–20, 1955 ... Winnipeg* (Ottawa: Fisheries Council of Canada, n.d.), pp. 23–25.

14 J.J. Van West, "Independent Fishermen," pp. 163–64.

15 W.A. Kennedy, *Daily Catch Record*, Vol. 1, p. 16; CCI, *Report*, p. 28; Ken Cox et al., "The Rehabilitation of the Inland Commercial Fisheries. Background Material," MS on file, Library, Dept. of Fisheries and Oceans, Ottawa, 1978, p. 99.

Ownership and Marketing

1 CPCL, *Crown Lands ... 1859*, App. 30.

2 Ibid.; NA, RG1, L3, Vol. 412, P3/30 (reel C-2734).

3 CPCL, *Crown Lands ... 1859*, App. 31, p. 85.

4 Ibid., *1857*, p. 70; CDFC, *Dominion Fisheries Commission ... Ontario*, pp. 42–45.

5 NA, RG1, L3, Vol. 409, P20/13 (reel C-2732); CPCL, *Crown Lands ... 1857*, p. 88.

6 NA, RG1, L3, Vol. 34, Land Book P; ibid., Vol. 356, M17/363; ibid., Vol. 259a, IJ18/59 and 59b; ibid., Vol. 416, P7/7.

7 T.H. Whillans, "Fish Community," p. 185.

8 CPLA, *Journals of the Legislative Assembly ... 1858* (Montreal: Rollo Campbell, 1859), App. 21, Report of the Special Commission Appointed to Investigate Indian Affairs in Canada: Report upon the Present State of Great Manitoulin Island (hereafter cited as Report upon Manitoulin).

9 G.L. Nute, "American Fur Company," pp. 496–501; NA, MG20, B.194/b/10, p. 17, Mource to Newberry, 8 Nov. 1835; NA, MG20, B.194/b/11, p. 7, Mource to Bethune, 16 June 1836; NA, MG20, B.194/b/14, pp. 20–22, Mource to Simpson, 29 Aug. 1839.

10 CDFC, *Dominion Fisheries Commission ... Ontario*, Pt. 1, pp. 3–5, 29–32.

11 CPHC, *Debates*, 14 Feb. 1884, pp. 300–03.

12 CDFC, *Dominion Fisheries Commission ... Ontario*, Pt. 1, pp. 123–28.

13 CMF, *List of Shipping Issued by the Department of Marine and Fisheries; Being a List of Vessels on the Registry Books of the Dominion of Canada on the 31st Day of December 1892* (Ottawa: S.E. Dawson, Queen's Printer, 1893).

14 CDFC, *Dominion Fisheries Commission ... Ontario*, Pt. 1, pp. 61–66; W.A. Kennedy, *History of Commercial Fishing*, p. 28.

15 CPHC, *Debates*, 27 March 1893, pp. 3188–98, 3190.

16 CDFC, *Dominion Fisheries Commission ... Ontario*, Pt. 1, pp. 97–106.

17 NA, RG23, Vol. 221, File 1196-2, Johnston Inquiry, testimony of Charles Duffy; ibid., Vol. 222, File 1196, "Proceedings," Vol. 3, William Lount to (?), 4 April 1902; CF, *Annual Report ... 1888*, pp. 195–205.

18 CPCL, *Crown Lands ... 1858*, pp. 67–71.

19 CMF, *Annual Report ... 1871*, pp. 102–7.

20 OF, *Annual Report ... 1900*, p. 11; ibid., *1905*, pp. 13–14.

21 OGF, *Annual Report ... 1918*, pp. 8–9; ibid., *1919*, p. 8; ibid., *1920*, p. 10; ibid., *1921*, p. 11; ibid., *1922*, p. 7.

22 Hugh M. Smith, "Report on the Fisheries of Lake Ontario," *Bulletin of the United States Fish Commission for 1890*, Vol. 10 (1891), pp. 183–84.

23 William Robert Wightman, *Forever on the Fringe: Six Studies in the Development of Manitoulin Island* (Toronto: Univ. of Toronto Press, 1982) (hereafter cited as *Forever on the Fringe*), p. 96; NA, RG23, Vol. 221, File 1196-2, Johnston Inquiry, testimony of

James Clark; NA, RG23, Vol. 114, File 120, Pt. 1, pp. 31–39, memorandum by S. Wilmot, 22 Feb. 1894.

24 John L. Goodier, *The Fish and Fisheries of Canadian Lake Superior* (Toronto: Institute for Environmental Studies, Univ. of Toronto, 1982) (hereafter cited as *Fisheries of Canadian Lake Superior*), pp. 16, 47; "Fishery Interests Combine," *Times* (New York), 22 June 1898, p. 10; "The New Fishery Trust," *Times* (New York), 2 Oct. 1898, p. 5; J. Peters, "Commercial Fishing in Lake Huron," p. 118.

25 Canada, *The Canada Gazette*, 29 April 1899, pp. 211–12; J.L. Goodier, *Fisheries of Canadian Lake Superior*, p. 16; OA, RG49, I-7-B-2, Ontario Sessional Papers, 1913, No. 53, "Return of correspondence re: granting of a permit to Dominion Fish Co. to fish in Lizard Is. preserve."

26 NA, RG33, No. 79, Vol. 2, Dun and Bradstreet analytical report, ca. 1963.

27 One of the questions that the Ontario Game and Fisheries Commission (1909) was directed to investigate was the existence of contracts between Ontario fishermen and foreign companies; another was whether the trust encouraged breaches of the law. Ontario. Game and Fisheries Commission, *Final Report of the Ontario Game and Fisheries Commission, 1909–1911...* (Toronto: printed by Order of the Legislative Assembly of Ontario, L.K. Cameron, 1912), Instructions and p. 15.

28 OF, *Annual Report ... 1905*, pp. 13–14; NA, RG23, Vol. 157, File 466, p. 9, petition dated 24 Aug. 1894.

29 *See* the Prosser case, CPHC, *Debates*, 27 March 1893, pp. 3183–98, and the case of D.E. Macdowell, NA, RG23, Vol. 190, File 848.

30 A.E. Crewe, "Pound Net Fishing in Lake Erie Between Point Pelee and Rondeau," *The Canadian Fisherman*, Vol. 5, No. 3 (March 1918), pp. 660–62.

31 W.A. Kennedy, *History of Commercial Fishing*, p. 28.

32 J.L. Goodier, *Fisheries of Canadian Lake Superior*, pp. 41–42.

33 N.S. Cornell "Co-operation in the Fishing Industry," *The Canadian Fisherman*, Vol. 3, No. 11 (Nov. 1916), pp. 356–58; "The Utilization of Fish Waste — A New Industry for Port Stanley," *The Canadian Fisherman*, Vol. 5, No. 3 (March 1918), pp. 558–59; Ontario, *The Ontario Gazette*, 14 Sept. 1912, p. 1302, and 21 March 1914, p. 464.

34 Ontario. Dept. of Economics and Development. Special Research and Surveys Branch, "The Lake Erie Fishing Industry, Report Dealing with Representations Made to the Provincial Government in 1962," April 1963, MS on file, Library, Ontario Ministry of Natural Resources, Toronto.

35 Ohio. State University, Bowling Green. University Library. Center for Archival Collections, Wheeler and Company, Account Books, Vol. 1, p. 124; NA, RG23, Vol. 926, File 721-4-5(1), petition from the Pond Net Fishermen's Association of South Essex, 7 Sept. 1913.

36 NA, RG23, Vol. 926, File 721-4-5(2), 10–11 Feb. 1916; "Lake Erie Fishermen's Association Convention," *The Canadian Fisherman*, Vol. 4, No. 2 (Feb. 1917), pp. 52–53; "The Lake Huron and Georgian Bay Fisherman's Association," *The Canadian Fisherman*, Vol. 5, No. 3 (March 1918), p. 635.

37 J.J. Van West, "Independent Fishermen," pp. 96–99.

38 *The Canadian Fisherman* regularly reported on the Lake Erie Fishermen's Association conventions in its February or March issues during the 1920s.

39 NA, RG23, Vol. 927, File 721-4-5(8), questionnaire in Robinson to director of Naval Services, 12 Nov. 1920; ibid., Vol. 926, File 721-4-5(2), proceedings of the Lake Erie Fisherman's Association, 10–11 Feb. 1916; ibid., File 721-4-5(6), 12 Nov. 1920.

40 "Lake Erie Fisherman's Convention," *The Canadian Fisherman*, Vol. 8, No. 2 (Feb. 1921), pp. 36–39. Until 1915, gill-net fishermen had been required to fish off the county for which they were licensed. NA, RG23, Vol. 927, File 721-4-5(6), Robinson to director of Naval Services, 12 Nov. 1920; OGF, *Annual Report ... 1915*, p. 5.

41 "Special Meeting of Association Executive," *The Canadian Fisherman*, Vol. 13 (Feb. 1926), pp. 66–67.

42 OA, RG1, HB, Vol. 1, p. 130, "Fishermen Split Over Erie Ruling," *Daily Mail and Empire* (Toronto), 24 Jan. 1931; "Lake Erie Fishermen Meet in Convention," *Canadian Fisherman*, Vol. 19, No. 2 (Feb. 1932), p. 27.

43 OA, RG1, HB, Vol. 2, p. 149, "Commercial Fishing Changes Demanded," *Daily Mail and Empire* (Toronto), 9 Nov. 1934.

44 Ibid., Vol. 3, p. 50, unidentified newspaper, Dunnville, 12 March 1937, "New Fishing Edict Seen as a Detriment."

45 J.J. Van West, "Independent Fishermen," pp. 69, 78–80.

46 Ibid., pp. 75–76.

47 NA, RG20, Vol. 232, F31093, Cole to Wilgress, 21 May 1937.

48 "Annual Convention of the Lake Erie Fisheries Association," *The Canadian Fisherman*, Vol. 5, No. 3 (March 1918), pp. 640–50, resolutions; NA, RG20, Vol. 232, File 31093.

49 "Erie Fishermen Co-operating," *The Canadian Fisherman*, Vol. 10, No. 2 (Feb. 1923), p. 41; OA, RG1, HB, Vol. 3, p. 37, "Ontario Fishing Industry is Menaced by Poachers," *Times Journal* (St. Thomas, Ont.), 29 Jan. 1937; J.J. Van West, "Independent Fishermen," pp. 131–48; Ontario. Dept. of Economics and Development. Special Research and Surveys Branch, "The Lake Erie Fishing Industry, Report Dealing with Representations Made to the Provincial Government in 1962," April 1963, MS on file, Library, Ontario Ministry of Natural Resources, Toronto.

50 J.J. Van West, "Independent Fishermen," pp. 107–109.

51 "The Kolbe Years," *The Great Lakes Fisherman*, Vol. 9, No. 12 (Oct. 1982), pp. 17–30; Carl F. Kolbe, "The Industrial Situation of the Great Lakes Fisheries," in Ontario. Research Council. Advisory Committee of Fisheries and Wildlife, *Great Lakes Fisheries Symposium, 6–7 November, 1952* (Toronto: 1952), App C.8; J.J. Van West, "Independent Fishermen," pp. 105–06, 132, states that the family came from Lorain, Ohio.

52 J.J. Van West, "Independent Fishermen," pp. 148–56.

53 Ibid., pp. 164–66.

54 J.L. Goodier, *Fisheries of Canadian Lake Superior*, pp. 25–26, 31–33, 41–42.

Labour and Working Conditions

1 CDFC, *Dominion Fisheries Commission ... Ontario*, Pt. 1, pp. 57–58; NA, RG23, Vol. 244, File 1556, petition, Dec. 1898; Canada. Royal Commission on the Relations of Labour and Capital, *Report...* (Ottawa: Queen's Printer, A. Senecal, 1889), Vol.: Evidence, Ontario, pp. 379–84.

2 CPCL, *Crown Lands ... 1859*, App. 30, p. 83.

3 Ibid., *1857*, p. 77.

4 CDFC, *Dominion Fisheries Commission ... Ontario*, Pt. 1, pp. 42–45; Canada. Royal Commission on the Relations of Labour and Capital, *Report...* (Ottawa: Queen's Printer,

A. Senecal, 1889), Vol.: Evidence, Ontario, pp. 379–84; T.H. Whillans, "Fish Community," p. 185; NA, RG1, L3, Vol. 409, p. 20/13, reel C-2732.

5   CDFC, *Dominion Fisheries Commission ... Ontario*, Pt. 1, pp. 3–6, 29–32.

6   Hubert H. Gallagher, et al., *International Board of Inquiry for the Great Lakes Fisheries*, transcript of hearings at St. Thomas, pp. 40–41.

7   Ohio. State University, Bowling Green. University Library, Center for Archival Collections, McLean Brothers Fishery, Wage Book, Vol. 3, 1947–49.

8   William F. Sinclair, *The Federal Small Craft Harbours Program on Lake Erie: The Socio-Economic Need for the Program and its Potential for Success* ([Ottawa]: Small Craft Harbours Branch, Fisheries and Marine Service, Dept. of Fisheries and the Environment, 1978) (hereafter cited as *Small Craft Harbours Program*), Table 32.

9   NA, RG23, Vol. 926, File 721-4-5(1), petition from the fishermen of Tobermory, 9 Oct. 1914.

10 J.W. Milner, "Fisheries of the Great Lakes," pp. 2–3; H.M. Smith and M.-M. Snell, comp., "Fisheries of the Great Lakes in 1885," p. 220; J. Peters, "Commercial Fishing in Lake Huron," pp. 76, 115.

11 CPCL, *Crown Lands ... 1859*, App. 31; CPLA, Report upon Manitoulin.

12 H.M. Smith and M.-M. Snell, comp., "Fisheries of the Great Lakes in 1885," p. 220.

13 CDFC, *Dominion Fisheries Commission ... Ontario*, Pt. 1, pp. 118, 145–46.

14 William E. Meehan, "The Fish Industry of Lake Erie," in Pennsylvania. Board of Fish Commissioners, *Report of the Fish Commissioners of the State of Pennsylvania, for the year 1902* (Harrisburg: W.S. Ray, State Printer, 1902), p. 102; USTC, *Lake Fish*, p. 37.

15 Larry S. Lambert, *Ontario's Lake Erie Commercial Fishery: A Social and Economic Profile* ([Toronto]: Commercial Fish and Fur Branch, Division of Fish and Wildlife, Ontario Ministry of Natural Resources, 1975) (hereafter cited as *Ontario's Lake Erie Commercial Fishery*), p. 8.

16 J.J. Van West, "Independent Fishermen," pp. 122–23, 190–94; Hal Masson, "Gang O'Nets," *Maclean's Magazine*, 1 July 1946.

17 J.J. Van West, "Independent Fishermen," pp. 92–93.

18 USTC, *Lake Fish*, p. 37.

19 H.H. Gallagher et al., *International Board of Inquiry*, transcript of hearings at St. Thomas, pp. 40-41; USTC, *Lake Fish*, pp. 142, 144.

20 NA, RG23, Vol. 573, File 704-8-8(7), McNab to Rob, 30 Sept. 1922.

21 OA, RG1, HB, Vol. 4, p. 205, "Fishery Employees Strike over Pay," *Evening Telegram* (Toronto), 7 Oct. 1939.

22 J.L. Goodier, *Fisheries of Canadian Lake Superior*, p. 25.

23 J.J. Van West, "Independent Fishermen," p. 148. In November 1984 the firm was purchased by John Labatt Ltd.; family members were to remain on as managers.

24 G.B. Goode, "History and Methods of the Fisheries," p. 704.

25 "Women Taking the Place of Men," *The Canadian Fisherman*, Vol. 29, No. 12 (Dec. 1942), p. 23.

26 L.S. Lambert, *Ontario's Lake Erie Commercial Fishery*, p. 13; W.F. Sinclair, *Small Craft Harbours Program*, Table 12:1.

27 Hal Masson, "Gang O'Nets," *Maclean's Magazine*, 1 July 1946, pp. 19, 34–37.

28 NA, RG23, Vol. 244, File 1556, p. 349.

29 CDFC, *Dominion Fisheries Commission ... Ontario*, Pt. 2, testimony of Thomas Boyton, Joseph Gantry, William MacLeod.

30   CMF, *Annual Report ... 1879*, Pt. 1, p. 323; CDFC, *Dominion Fisheries Commission ...
     Ontario*, Pt. 1, pp. 221-26; NA, RG33, No. 79, Vol. 6, p. 832, Omstead testimony.
31   W.A. Kennedy, *Daily Catch Record*, Vol. 1, pp. 1–3.

Changes in Fish Stocks

1   CF, *Annual Report ... 1888*, pp. 195–205; CDFC, *Dominion Fisheries Commission ...
    Ontario*, Pt. 1, pp. 261–67.
2   W.B. Scott and E.J. Crossman, *Freshwater Fishes of Canada* (Ottawa: Fisheries Re-
    search Board of Canada, 1973) (hereafter cited as *Freshwater Fishes*), p. 193; J.R. Dy-
    mond, "Fisheries of the Great Lakes," p. 86.
3   W.J.R. Harkness and J.R. Dymond, *The Lake Sturgeon; The History of Its Fishery and
    Problems of Conservation* ([Toronto]: Fish and Wildlife Branch, Ontario Dept. of Lands
    and Forests, 1961)
4   Thomas Huxley Langlois, *The Western End of Lake Erie and its Ecology* (Ann Arbor:
    J.W. Edwards, 1954), pp. 290–97, 349; "Research Proves Commercial Fishermen
    Right," *The Great Lakes Fisherman*, Vol. 8, No. 7 (May 1981), p. 15; H.A. Regier and
    W.L. Hartman, "Lake Erie's Fish Community," p. 1252.
5   Ralph Hile, "Trends in the Lake Trout Fishery of Lake Huron through 1946," *Transac-
    tions of the American Fisheries Society*, Vol. 76 (1946), pp. 122–23.
6   D. Cucin and H.A. Regier, "Dynamics and Exploitation of Lake Whitefish in Southern
    Georgian Bay," *Journal of the Fisheries Research Board of Canada*, Vol. 23, No. 2
    (Feb. 1966), p. 229.

Post-Confederation
Legislation, Management, and Conservation

1   NA, RG23, Vol. 190, File 848, p. 3, Macdonnell to Tupper, 15 Sept. 1893.
2   Ibid., 24 April 1897; ibid., Vol. 323, File 2753, memo by Prince re "Fish Monopoly."
3   CF, *Annual Report ... 1888*, p. xii; CMF, *Annual Report ... 1892*, p. 20; CGB, *Domin-
    ion Fisheries Commission ... Georgian Bay*, p. 37.
4   NA, RG23, Vol. 157, File 466, p. 7, Kerr to deputy minister, 19 Dec. 1893.
5   Ibid., Vol. 507, File 709-12-2(1), order-in-council 2351 of 29 Nov. 1919.
6   CF, *Annual Report ... 1889*, pp. xxxiii; R.P. Gillis, "Early Regulatory Records and the
    History of Science and Technology: The Case of the Sawdust Pollution Files, 1866–
    1902," in Richard A. Jarrell and Norman R. Ball, eds., *Science, Technology, and
    Canadian History* (Waterloo, Ont.: Wilfrid Laurier Univ. Press, n.d.), pp. 60–71.
7   CF, *Annual Report ... 1888*, pp. 195–205; CDFC, *Dominion Fisheries Commission ...
    Ontario*, Pt. 1, pp. 262.
8   Fikret Berkes and Dorothy Pocock, *Issues and Conflicts in Fisheries Management of
    Lake Erie* (St. Catharines, Ont.: Institute of Urban and Environmental Studies, Brock
    Univ., 1980) (hereafter cited as *Issues and Conflicts*), pp. 50–51.
9   CPHC, *Debates*, 27 March 1893, p. 3204.
10 *See* NA, RG23, Vol. 224, File 1241.
11 J. Peters, "Commercial Fishing in Lake Huron," p. 107.
12 CMF, *Annual Report ... 1905*, pp. 313–14.
13 CPCL, *Crown Lands ... 1858*, p. 81.
14 CMF, *Annual Report ... 1905*, pp. lxxxiv–xcl; Archibald Gowanlock Huntsman, "Why
    Did the Ontario Salmon Disappear?" *Proceedings and Transactions of the Royal Society
    of Canada*, 3rd ser., Vol. 38, Sect. 5 (1944), pp. 83–102.

15 CMF, *Annual Report ... 1894*, pp. 379; OGF, *Annual Report ... 1926*, p. 4.

16 Seth W. Downing, 'A Plan for Promoting the Whitefish Production of the Great Lakes,' in "Proceedings of the Fourth International Fishery Congress: Organization and Sessional Business, Papers and Discussions Held at Washington, U.S.A.: September 22 to 26, 1908," *Bulletin of the Bureau of Fisheries*, Vol. 28—1908, Pt. 1 (1910), pp. 630–32.

17 Paul Roby Reighard, 'A Plan for Promoting the Whitefish Production of the Great Lakes,' in "Proceedings of the Fourth International Fishery Congress: Organization and Sessional Business, Papers and Discussions Held at Washington, U.S.A.: September 22 to 26, 1908," *Bulletin of the Bureau of Fisheries*, Vol. 28—1908, Pt. 1 (1910) pp. 682–83.

18 CMF, *Annual Report ... 1879*, pp. 35–40; ibid., *1881*, pp. 11–12.

19 W.F. Whitcher, "Practical Results of Fish Culture in the Dominion of Canada," *Forest and Stream*, Vol. 20, No. 21 (21 June 1883), p. 408.

20 OGF, *Annual Report ... 1927*, p. 4.

21 Archibald Gowanlock Huntsman, "Fishery Management and Research," in Ontario. Research Council. Advisory Committee of Fisheries and Wildlife, *Great Lakes Fisheries Symposium, 6–7 November 1952* (Toronto: 1952), App. C.8; K.J. Chambers, "Fish Culture — From Art to Science," *Ontario Fish and Wildlife Review*, Vol. 10, Nos. 3–4 (Fall–Winter 1971) (hereafter cited as "Fish Culture"), p. 18; John Richardson Dymond, "Artificial Propagation in the Management of the Great Lakes," *Transactions of the American Fisheries Society*, Vol. 86 (1956), pp. 384–91.

22 OGF, *Annual Report ... 1927 to ... 1945/46*; OLF, *Annual Report ... 1947 to ... 1972*; ONR, *Annual Report ... 1973 to ... 1981*.

23 CMF, *Annual Report ... 1874*, p. 180.

24 W.B. Scott and E.J. Crossman, *Freshwater Fishes*, pp. 149, 160, 174; pers. com., W.J. Christie.

25 W.B. Scott and E.J. Crossman, *Freshwater Fishes*, p. 408.

26 CMF, *Annual Report ... 1881*, Supplement No. 2, pp. 11–12.

27 Ibid., ... *1896*, Supplement No. 1, p. 29.

28 W.B. Scott and E.J. Crossman, *Freshwater Fishes*, p. 313.

29 Ibid., pp. 121–23; Norman S. Baldwin et al., *Commercial Fish Production in the Great Lakes, 1867–1977* (Ann Arbor: Great Lakes Fishery Commission, 1979) (hereafter cited as *Commercial Fish Production*), p. 126; Frank N. Egerton, *Overfishing or Pollution? Case History of a Controversy on the Great Lakes* (Ann Arbor: Great Lakes Fishery Commission, 1985), p. 21.

30 W.B. Scott and E.J. Crossman, *Freshwater Fishes*, pp. 70–71.

31 K.J. Chambers, "Fish Culture," p. 18.

32 Lee Emery, *Review of Fish Species Introduced into the Great Lakes, 1819–1974* (Ann Arbor: Great Lakes Fishery Commission, 1985), pp. 4–5; N.S. Baldwin et al., *Commercial Fish Production*, pp. 22, 28.

33 NA, RG32, C-2, Vol. 218, E.E. Prince File.

34 G. Bruce Woodland, "The Fisheries Research Board of Canada," *Fisheries Council of Canada, Annual Review* (1967), pp. 53–55.

35 Kenneth Johnstone, *The Aquatic Explorers: A History of the Fisheries Research Board of Canada* (Toronto: Univ. of Toronto Press, 1977), pp. 46–51.

36 N. Robert Payne, "A Century of Commercial Fishery Administration in Ontario," *Ontario Fish and Wildlife Review*, Vol. 6, Nos. 1–2 (Spring–Summer 1967), p. 10.
37 Ibid., p. 14; S. Kendall, J.R. Payne, and W.F. Sinclair, "Lake Erie Fisheries," p. 23.

Federal and Provincial
Jurisdictions

1 *Robertson v. The Queen* (1882), in Canada. Supreme Court, *Supreme Court of Canada Reports...*, Vol. 6 (Ottawa: Printed by Maclean Roger and Co., 1882), p. 52.
2 Ontario. Laws and Statutes, etc., *Statutes of the Province of Ontario...* (Toronto: John Notman, Queen's Printer, 1885), "An Act to Regulate the Fisheries of this Province," 48 Vict., c. 9, 1885.
3 Canada. Dept. of Fisheries, *Status of Fishing Rights in Inland and Non-Navigable Waters of Canada: Jurisdiction of Local and Federal Authorities in Connection Therewith* (Ottawa: Brown Chamberlin, Queen's Printer, 1891), pp. 1–16; NA, RG23, Vol. 123, File 164, Pt. 1, 26 June 1895 and 1 May 1896; *see* fisheries overseers' reports in Ontario. Dept. of Crown Lands, *Report of the Commissioner of Crown Lands...* (Toronto: imprint varies, 1887–94).
4 Ontario. Game and Fish Commission [Commission to Enquire upon the Game and Fish of the Province of Ontario and the Laws Relating to their Protection], *Commissioners' Report* (Toronto: Printed by order of the Legislative Assembly of Ontario, Warwick and Sons, 1892), pp. 194–95, 308.
5 NA, RG23, Vol. 123, File 164, Pt. 1, pp. 147–52.
6 CMF, *Annual Report ... 1899*, p. ix.
7 R.S. Lambert and P. Pross, *Renewing Nature's Wealth*, p. 451.
8 NA, RG23, Vol. 123, File 164, 9 June 1899 and 23 June 1899.
9 Ibid., Vol. 327, File 2787, Bastedo to Prince, 9 Feb. 1903.
10 OGF, *Annual Report ... 1910*, p. 6; CMF, *Annual Report ... 1910–11*, 1910–11, p. xxxiii and App. 7, Inspector Duncan's Report; NA, RG23, Vol. 123, File 164, p. 3, Sheppard to Venning, 6 Jan. 1908.
11 Elmer Higgins, "The Ineffectiveness of Regulation of the Great Lakes Fisheries by the Individual States," in United States. Council of State Governments. Central Secretariat, *Proceedings of the Great Lakes Fisheries Conference, Detroit, Michigan, February 25–26, 1938* (Chicago: n.d.) (hereafter cited as "Ineffectiveness of Legslation"), p. 45.
12 NA, RG23, Vol. 1355, File 731-1-26(1); ibid., Vol. 580, File 740-19-2, Hazen to Thornton, 9 Jan. 1915; Canada. Dept. of Marine and Fisheries. Fisheries Branch, *Annual Report on Fish Culture, 1925* (Ottawa: F.A. Acland, King's Printer, 1926), pp. 10–11. For dates of opening and closing of hatcheries, *see* annual departmental reports, 1911–12 to 1915–16.
13 Henry A. Regier, Vernon C. Applegate, and Richard A. Rider, *The Ecology and Management of the Walleye in Western Lake Erie* (Ann Arbor: Great Lakes Fishery Commission, 1969), pp. 85–86.
14 NA, RG23, Vol. 224, File 1241 generally.
15 Ibid., Vol. 139, File 317, copy of order-in-council of 13 Aug. 1903; OGF, *Annual Report ... 1907*, pp. 6–7.
16 NA, RG23, Vol. 926, 721-4-5(1), memorandum of 12 June 1915.
17 Ibid.
18 "The New Fishery Trust," *Times* (New York), 2 Oct. 1898, p. 5, col. 5.

19   Canada, *The Canada Gazette*, Supplement, 21 Sept. 1907, pp. 60–63, Special Fishery Regulations, Province of Ontario; ibid, 29 April 1922, Special Fishery Regulations for the Province of Ontario.

20   Canada. Laws and Statutes, etc., *Statutes*, 31 Vict., c. 60, s.9.2, 1868. Regulations established by the Province of Ontario in 1899 provided minimum size limits, two pounds, for lake trout and whitefish, but the federal government considered the regulations to be ultra vires and it is doubtful that they were enforced.

21   CF, *Annual Report ... 1888*, pp. 195–205; NA, RG23, Vol. 105, File 94, notice re.: mesh size, 13 April 1893.

22   NA, RG23, Vol. 926, File 721-4-5(2), petition from Port Maitland fishermen, 2 July 1915; ibid., Vol. 927, File 721-4-5(2), Kolbe et al. to deputy minister of Naval Service, 19 Dec. 1921.

23   Ibid., Vol. 121, File 141, deputy minister to L. Wigle, 30 Dec. 1893.

24   F. Berkes and D. Pocock, *Issues and Conflicts*, pp. 10–11; W.J. Christie, *North American Experience*, p. 12.

25   NA, RG23, Vol. 114, File 120, p. 90, E.E. Prince memorandum, 1898.

26   Ibid., Vol. 927, File 721-4-5(6), Robinson to director of Naval Services, 12 Nov. 1920.

27   OA, RG1, HB, Vol. 3, p. 50, unidentified newspaper, Dunnville, 12 March 1937, "New Fishing Edict Seen as a Detriment."

28   W.F. Sinclair, *Small Craft Harbours Program*, Map 2.

29   "Annual Convention of the Lake Erie Fisheries Association," *The Canadian Fisherman*, Vol. 5, No. 3 (March 1918), pp. 640–50.

30   *See* reports on revenues from Ontario commercial fisheries in OGF, *Annual Reports*.

31   "News and Notes from Inland Waters," *The Canadian Fisherman* (April 1925), pp. 92–93; "Around the Great Lakes," *The Canadian Fisherman* (Sept. 1925), pp. 283–84.

32   J.J. Van West, *Independent Fishermen*, pp. 155–62.

33   E. Higgins, "Ineffectiveness of Regulation," pp. 49–50.

34   H.A. Regier and W.L. Hartman, "Lake Erie's Fish Community," pp. 1249, 1251–52.

35   Pers. com., J. Tilt, Commercial Development Co-ordinator, Fisheries Branch, Ontario Ministry of Natural Resources.

International Jurisdiction

1   For examples *see* CF, *Annual Report ... 1890*, p. xlix, and "Letters to the Editor," *The Canadian Fisherman*, Vol. 15, No. 2 (Feb. 1928), pp. 42–44, 47–48.

2   D.W. Lewis, *Lake Erie Commercial Fishing*, pp. 134–38.

3   E. Higgins, "Ineffectiveness of Regulation," p. 56.

4   JFC, *Report of the Joint Commission*.

5   Don Courtney Piper, *The International Law of the Great Lakes: A Study of Canadian–United States Co-Operation* (Durham, N.C.: Commonwealth Studies Center, Duke Univ. Press, 1967), pp. 39–41.

6   Ibid., pp. 74–76.

7   "Lake Erie Fishery Advisory Committee Active," *Fisheries Service Bulletin*, No. 212 (3 Jan. 1933), pp. 1–2; "Bureau Aids in Securing Uniform Fishery Legislation on Lake Erie," *Fisheries Service Bulletin*, No. 216 (1 May 1933), p. 2; "Unified Control of Lake Erie Fisheries Proposed," *Fisheries Service Bulletin*, No. 234 (1 Nov. 1933), pp. 3–4.

8   International Board of Inquiry for the Great Lakes Fisheries, ... *Report and Supplement*, Hubert H. Gallagher et al. (Washington, D.C.: USGPO, 1943); Canada. Treaties, etc., *Great Lakes Fisheries. Convention between Canada and the United States of America*

signed at Washington, April 2, 1946 (Ottawa: Edmond Cloutier, King's Printer, 1946); "Wisconsin and Ohio Pass Resolutions Against U.S.–Canada Pact," *The Fisherman*, Vol. 15, No. 5 (May 1947), p. 9.

9   Canada. Treaties, etc., *Great Lakes Fisheries. Convention between Canada and the United States of America signed at Washington, September 10, 1954* (Ottawa: Roger Duhamel, Queen's Printer, 1961).

10   D.W. Lewis, *Lake Erie Commercial Fishing*, pp. 105–06.

11   United States. General Accounting Office. Comptroller General of the United States, *The U.S. Great Lakes Commercial Fishing Industry — Past, Present and Potential...* (Washington, D.C.: USGPO, 1977) (hereafter cited as *The U.S. Great Lakes Commercial Fishing Industry*), p. 10; S. Kendall, J.R. Payne and W.F. Sinclair, "Lake Erie Fisheries."

Commercial, Sport and Subsistence Fisheries

1   CPHC, *Debates*, 14 Feb. 1884, p. 299.

2   G.A. Macdonald, "Saulteur-Ojibway Fishery," pp. 78, 114.

3   CPCL, *Crown Lands ... 1857*, pp. 72–76; CPLA, Report upon Manitoulin; NA, RG10, Vol. 1967, File 1875, Van Abbott to minister of the Interior.

4   W.R. Wightman, *Forever on the Fringe*, pp. 101–02; NA, RG10, Vol. 1967, File 1875, Vol. 2184, File 36918, and Vol. 2185, File 37135.

5   CPLA, Report upon Manitoulin.

6   Finlay Macdiarmid, B.A. Bensley, C.A. Canadee, *Report of Special Committee on the Game Fish Situation* (Toronto: Herbert H. Ball, King's Printer, 1930) (hereafter cited as *Special Committee on Game Fish*), pp. 105–06.

7   D.H. Loftus, *Charterboat Fishery*.

8   Vernon C. Applegate and H.D. Van Meter, *A Brief History of Commercial Fishing in Lake Erie* (Washington, D.C.: U.S. Fish and Wildlife Service, 1970), p. 22.

9   D.W. Lewis, *Lake Erie Commercial Fishing*, pp. 38–41.

10   F. McDiarmid, B.A. Bensley and C.A. Canadee, *Special Committee on Game Fish*, p. 63.

11   Daniel R. Talhelm et al., *Current Estimates of Great Lakes Fisheries Values: 1979 Status Report* (Ann Arbor: Great Lakes Fishery Commission, 1979), p. 2.

12   United States. General Accounting Office. Comptroller General of the United States, *The U.S. Great Lakes Commercial Fishing Industry*, p. 10; Ken Schultz, "The Great Great Lakes," *Field and Stream*, Vol. 87, No. 10, North East Edition (Feb. 1983), p. 82; S. Kendall, J.R. Payne, and W.F. Sinclair, "Lake Erie Fisheries," p. 25.

References Cited

Adams, G.F., and D.P. Kolenosky
Out of the Water: Ontario's Freshwater Fish Industry. Commercial Fish and Fur Branch, Ontario Ministry of Natural Resources, [Toronto], 1974.

American Fisheries Society
A List of Common and Scientific Names of Fishes from the United States and Canada. By C. Richard Robins et al. (Committee on Names of Fishes). 4th ed. Bethseda, Maryland, 1980. American Fisheries Society, Special Publication No. 12.

Annual Statistical Review of Canadian Fisheries/Revue statistique annuelle des pêches canadiennes
Title and imprint vary. Vols. 1–12 (1969–80). Ottawa.

Applegate, Vernon C., and H.D. Van Meter
A Brief History of Commercial Fishing in Lake Erie. U.S. Fish and Wildlife Service, Washington, D.C., 1970. Fishery Leaflet No. 630.

Baldwin, Norman S., et al.
Commercial Fish Production in the Great Lakes, 1867–1977. Great Lakes Fishery Commission, Ann Arbor, 1979. Great Lakes Fishery Commission, Technical Report No. 3.

Barry, James P.
Georgian Bay; The Sixth Great Lake. Clarke Irwin, Toronto, 1968.

Berkes, Fikret, and Dorothy Pocock
Issues and Conflicts in Fisheries Management of Lake Erie. Institute of Urban and Environmental Studies, Brock University, St. Catharines, Ont., 1980.

Bigsby, John Jeremiah
The Shoe and the Canoe; or, Pictures of Travel in the Canadas ... With Facts and Opinions on Emigration, State Policy, and Other Points of Public Interest.... Chapman and Hall, London, 1850. 2 vols. Vol. 2.

Buscombe, Donald A.
Port Dover Scenes. 2 vols. Vol. 1: Through Changing Times, 1860–1974. Erie Shore Publications, Port Stanley, Ont., [1974]. Vol. 2: A Tour through Yesteryear. Impressions, St. Thomas, Ont., [1976].

Campbell, Susan
Fort William: Living and Working at the Post. Fort William Archaeological Project, Ontario Ministry of Culture and Recreation, Toronto, 1976.

Canada
The Canada Gazette. 1899, 1907, 1922, 1925. Ottawa.
The Ontario Fishery Regulations and Amendments to March 1, 1980. Ontario Ministry of Natural Resources, [Toronto, 1980].

Canada. Commission of Inquiry into Freshwater Fish Marketing.
Report.... George H. McIvor. Queen's Printer, Ottawa, [1966].

Canada. Department of Fisheries.
Annual Report ... 1884 to *... 1891.* Imprint varies, Ottawa, 1885–92. (Continued by reports of the Department of Marine and Fisheries.)
Annual Report ... 1940–41. Edmond Cloutier, King's Printer, Ottawa, 1941.
Status of Fishing Rights in Inland and Non-Navigable Waters of Canada: Jurisdiction of Local and Federal Authorities in Connection Therewith. Brown Chamberlin, Queen's Printer, Ottawa, 1891.

Canada. Department of Marine and Fisheries.
Annual Report ... 1868 to *... 1883.* Title and imprint vary, Ottawa, 1869–84. (Continued by reports of the Department of Fisheries.)
... Annual Report ... 1892, Pt. 2, Fisheries to *... 1913–14, Fisheries.* Title and imprint vary, Ottawa, 1893–1914. (Continued by reports of the Department of the Naval Service, Fisheries Branch.)
List of Shipping Issued by the Department of Marine and Fisheries; Being a List of Vessels on the Registry Books of the Dominion of Canada on the 31st day of December 1892. S.E. Dawson, Queen's Printer, Ottawa, 1893.

Canada. Department of Marine and Fisheries. Fisheries Branch.
Annual Report on Fish Culture. 1925. F.A. Acland, King's Printer, Ottawa, 1926.

Canada. Department of the Naval Service. Fisheries Branch.
... Annual Report ... 1914–15 to *... 1916–17.* Imprint varies, Ottawa, 1915–17. (Continued by reports of the Department of Marine and Fisheries.)

Canada. Department of Trade and Commerce. Dominion Bureau of Statistics.
Fisheries Statistics.... Title and imprint vary, Ottawa, 1921–64.
Fisheries Statistics of Canada, 1931. F.A. Acland, King's Printer, Ottawa, 1932.
Seventh Census of Canada, 1931. J.O. Patenaude, King's Printer, Ottawa, 1933–42. 14 vols. Vol. 7: Occupations and Industry.

Canada. Dominion Bureau of Statistics.
Fisheries Statistics.... Title and imprint vary, Ottawa, 1965–70.

Canada. Dominion Fishery Commission.
Report of the Dominion Fishery Commission on the Fisheries of the Province of Ontario, 1893. Samuel Wilmot and Edward Harris. S.E. Dawson, Queen's Printer, Ottawa, 1894. 2 parts. Canada, Sessional Paper, 1893, No. 10c, Supplement to Vol. 26, No. 7.

Canada. Georgian Bay Fisheries Commission.
Report and Recommendations (with Appendices) of the Dominion Fisheries Commission Appointed to Enquire into the Fisheries of Georgian Bay and Adjacent Waters, 1905–1908. John Birnie, James J. Noble, and E.E. Prince. Government Printing Bureau, Ottawa, 1908.

Canada. Laws and Statutes, etc.
Statutes of Canada Passed in the Session Held in the Thirty-First Year of the Reign of Her Majesty Queen Victoria, Being the First Session of the Parliament of Canada, Part Second. Malcolm Cameron, Queen's Printer, Ottawa, 1868.

Canada. Ministry of Agriculture.
Census of Canada, 1880–81/Recensement du Canada. MacLean, Roger & Co., Ottawa, 1882–85. 4 vols. Vol. 2.

Canada. National Archives.
MG20, B.129, Hudson's Bay Company, North America Trading Post Records, Michipicoten.
MG20, B.194, Hudson's Bay Company, North America Trading Post Records, Sault Ste. Marie.
MG20, D.4, Hudson's Bay Company, Governors' Papers, George Simpson Correspondence.
RG1, E1, Executive Council, State Records.
RG1, L3, Executive Council, Land Records.

RG2, 1, Privy Council Office, Orders in Council.

RG10, Indian Affairs.

RG20, Trade and Commerce.

RG23, Fisheries and Oceans.

RG32, Public Service Commission, Historical Personnel Files.

RG33, No. 79, Royal Commissions, Records of the Commission of Inquiry into Freshwater Fish Marketing.

Canada. Parliament. House of Commons.
Official Report of the Debates of the House of Commons.... Queen's Printer, 1884–94, Ottawa.

Canada. Statistics Canada.
Fisheries Statistics of Canada: Canada Summary. Information Canada, Ottawa, 1971.
1971 Census of Canada, Volume Series. Ottawa, 1972–77. 9 vols. Vol. 3: Economic Characteristics.

Canada (Province). Board of Registration and Statistics.
Appendix to the First [Census] Report. Stewart Derbishire and George Desbarats, Queen's Printers, Montreal, 1849.
Census of the Canadas, 1851–52. Printed by John Lovell, Quebec, 1853–55. 2 vols.

Canada (Province). Department of Crown Lands.
Report of the Commissioner of Crown Lands of Canada for the Year 1857 to *Report ... 1866.* Title and imprint vary, Toronto, 1858–67.

Canada (Province). Legislative Assembly.
Journals of the Legislative Assembly ... 1858. Rollo Campbell, Montreal, 1859. Appendix 21, Report of the Special Commission Appointed to Investigate Indian Affairs in Canada: Report upon the Present State of Great Manitoulin Island.

Canada (Province). Parliament.
Statutes of the Province of Canada.... Imprint varies, 1841–58.

Canada. Royal Commission on the Relations of Labour and Capital.
Report of the Royal Commission on the Relations of Labour and Capital in Canada. A. Senecal, Queen's Printer, Ottawa, 1889. 6 vols.

Canada. Supreme Court.
Supreme Court of Canada Reports.... Vol. 6. Printed by Maclean, Roger and Co., Ottawa, 1882.

Canada. Treaties, etc.
Great Lakes Fisheries. Convention between Canada and the United States of America signed at Washington, April 2, 1946. Edmond Cloutier, King's Printer, Ottawa, 1946. Treaty Series, 1946, No. 13.
Great Lakes Fisheries. Convention between Canada and the United States of America signed at Washington, September 10, 1954. Roger Duhamel, Queen's Printer, Ottawa, 1961. Treaty Series, 1954, No. 19.

Canadian Fisheries Manual
"The Inland Fisheries." 1932, pp. 68–71. Gardenvale, Quebec.

The Canadian Fisherman **(Gardenvale, Quebec)**
'Quebec and Ontario.' In "The Fishing Industry of Canada and Newfoundland." Vol. 2, No. 9 (Sept. 1915), pp. 280–85.
"Lake Erie Fishermen's Association Convention." Vol. 4, No. 2 (Feb. 1917), pp. 52–53.
"The Utilization of Fish Waste — A New Industry for Port Stanley." Vol. 5, No. 3 (March 1918), pp. 558–59.
"The Lake Huron and Georgian Bay Fisherman's Association." Vol. 5, No. 3 (March 1918), p. 635.
"Annual Convention of the Lake Erie Fisheries Association." Vol. 5, No. 3 (March 1918), pp. 640–50.
"Lake Erie Fishermen's Convention." Vol. 8, No. 2 (Feb. 1921), pp. 36–39.
"Erie Fishermen Co-Operating." Vol. 10, No. 2 (Feb. 1923), p. 41.
"News and Notes from Inland Waters." April 1925, pp. 92–93.
"Around the Great Lakes." Sept. 1925, pp. 283–84.
"Special Meeting of Association Executive." Vol. 13 (Feb. 1926), pp. 66–67.
"Lake Erie Fishermen's Assn. Convention." Vol. 15, No. 2 (Feb. 1928), pp. 42–44.
"Letters to the Editor." Vol. 15, No. 2 (Feb. 1928), pp. 47–48.
"The Package Fish Trade in the U.S." Vol. 15, No. 8 (Aug. 1928), pp. 13–14, 32, 43, 44.
"History of Filleting." Vol. 16 (Aug. 1929), p. 34.
"Lake Erie Fishermen Meet in Convention." Vol. 19, No. 2 (Feb. 1932), p. 27.
"Women Taking the Place of Men." Vol. 29, No. 12 (Dec. 1942), p. 23.

Chambers, K.J.
"Fish Culture — From Art to Science." *Ontario Fish and Wildlife Review*, Vol. 10, Nos. 3–4 (Fall–Winter 1971), pp. 15–21. Toronto.

Chapelle, Howard Irving
American Small Sailing Craft: Their Design, Development, and Construction. W.W. Norton and Co., New York, 1951.

Christie, W.J.
A Study of Freshwater Fishery Regulations Based on North American Experience. Food and Agriculture Organization of the United Nations, Rome, 1978. FAO Fisheries Technical Paper No. 180.

Colvin, Thomas E.
"Main-Stay of the Great Lakes." *The Canadian Fisherman*, Vol. 46, No. 11 (Nov. 1959), pp. 38–41. Gardenvale, Quebec.

Cornell, N.S.
"Co-operation in the Fishing Industry." *The Canadian Fisherman*, Vol. 3, No. 11 (Nov. 1916), pp. 356–58. Gardenvale Quebec.

Cox, Ken, et al.
"The Rehabilitation of the Inland Commercial Fisheries. Background Material." Manuscript on file, Library, Department of Fisheries and Oceans, Ottawa, 1978.

Crewe, A.E.
"Pound Net Fishing in Lake Erie Between Point Pelee and Rondeau." *The Canadian Fisherman*, Vol. 5, No. 3 (March 1918), pp. 660–62. Gardenvale, Quebec.

Cucin, D., and H.A. Regier
"Dynamics and Exploitation of Lake Whitefish in Southern Georgian Bay." *Journal of the Fisheries Research Board of Canada*, Vol. 23, No. 2 (Feb. 1966), pp. 221–74. Ottawa.

Downing, Seth W.
'A Plan for Promoting the Whitefish Production of the Great Lakes.' In "Proceedings of the Fourth International Fishery Congress: Organization and Sessional Business, Papers and Discussions Held at Washington, U.S.A.: September 22 to 26, 1908," *Bulletin of the Bureau of Fisheries*, Vol. 28—1908, Pt. 1 (1910), pp. 630–32. Washington, D.C.

Dymond, John Richardson
"Artificial Propagation in the Management of the Great Lakes." *Transactions of the American Fisheries Society*, Vol. 86 (1956), pp. 384–91. St. Paul.
"The Fisheries of the Great Lakes." In J.R. Dymond, ed., *Fish and Wildlife; A Memorial to W.J.K. Harkness*, Longman's, Toronto, 1964, pp. 75–92.

Egerton, Frank N.
Overfishing or Pollution? Case History of a Controversy on the Great Lakes. Great Lakes Fishery Commission, Ann Arbor, 1985. Great Lakes Fishery Commission, Technical Report No. 41.

Ellsworth, Joan Lenore
"The Eastern Lake Ontario Commercial Fishery, 1673–1900: A Cultural Heritage, A Forgotten Staple." MA thesis, Queen's University, Kingston, 1983.

Emery, Lee
Review of Fish Species Introduced into the Great Lakes, 1819–1974. Great Lakes Fishery Commission, Ann Arbor, 1985. Great Lakes Fishery Commission, Technical Report No. 45.

Ferguson, R.G.
Lake Erie Commercial Fisheries: A Preliminary Appraisal. Ontario Department of Lands and Forests, [Toronto], 1955.

***Fisheries Service Bulletin* (Washington, D.C.)**
"Lake Erie Fishery Advisory Committee Active." No. 212 (3 Jan. 1933), pp. 1–2.
"Bureau Aids in Securing Uniform Fishery Legislation on Lake Erie." No. 216 (1 May 1933), p. 2.
"Unified Control of Lake Erie Fisheries Proposed." No. 234 (1 Nov. 1933), pp. 3–4.

***The Fisherman: The News Journal of the Great Lakes Fisheries* (Grand Haven, Mich.)**
"Death Claims Edward Crossley, Inventor of the Original Crossley Net Lifter." Vol. 15, No. 5 (May 1947), p. 18.
"Wisconsin and Ohio Pass Resolutions Against U.S.–Canada Pact." Vol. 15, No. 5 (May 1947), p. 9.

Fox, William Sherwood
The Bruce Beckons; The Story of Lake Huron's Great Peninsula. Drawings by Clare Bice and Vincent Elliott. University of Toronto Press, Toronto, 1952.
"The Literature of the Salmo Salar in Lake Ontario and Tributary Streams." *Proceedings and Transactions of the Royal Society of Canada*, 3rd ser., Vol. 24, Sect. 2 (1930), pp. 45–55. Toronto.

Gillis, R.P.
"Early Regulatory Records and the History of Science and Technology: The Case of the Sawdust Pollution Files, 1866–1902." In *Science, Technology, and Canadian History; The First Conference on the Study of the History of*

Canadian Science and Technology/Les Sciences, la technologie et l'histoire canadienne; Premier congrès sur l'histoire des sciences et de la technologie canadiennes, ed. Richard A. Jarrell and Norman R. Ball, Wilfrid Laurier University Press, Waterloo, Ont., n.d., pp. 60–71.

Goode, George Brown, et al.
"History and Methods of the Fisheries." In G.B. Goode et al., *The Fisheries and Fishery Industries of the United States. Prepared through the Co-Operation of the Commissioner of Fisheries and the Superintendent of the Tenth Census....*, U.S. Government Printing Office, Washington, D.C., 1884–87, 7 vols., Pt. 5. U.S. Congress. Senate, 47th Congress. 1st Sess., Misc. Doc. No. 124.

Goodier, John L.
The Fish and Fisheries of Canadian Lake Superior. Institute for Environmental Studies, University of Toronto, Toronto, 1982.

***The Great Lakes Fisherman* (Port Stanley, Ont.)**
"The United States Fresh Water Fishery Then and Now." Vol. 3, No. 8 (June 1976), pp. 13–30.
"Research Proves Commercial Fishermen Right." Vol. 8, No. 7 (May 1981), p. 15.
"The Kolbe Years." Vol. 9, No. 12 (Oct. 1982), pp. 17–30.

Hamilton, James Cleland
The Georgian Bay; An Account of its Position, Inhabitants, Mineral Interests, Fish, Timber, and Other Resources ... Papers Read before the Canadian Institute.... Carswell Co., Toronto, 1893.

Harkness, W.J.K., and J.R. Dymond
The Lake Sturgeon; the History of Its Fishery and Problems of Conservation. Fish and Wildlife Branch, Ontario Department of Lands and Forests, [Toronto], 1961.

Hatcher, Harlan H.
The Great Lakes. The Oxford University Press, London, 1944.

Higgins, Elmer
"The Ineffectiveness of Regulation of the Great Lakes Fisheries by the Individual States." In United States. Council of State Governments. Central Secretariat, *Proceedings of the Great Lakes Fisheries Conference, Detroit, Michigan, February 25–26, 1938*, Chicago, n.d., pp. 48–60. Typescript.

Hile, Ralph
"Trends in the Lake Trout Fishery of Lake Huron through 1946." *Transactions of the American Fisheries Society,* Vol. 76 (1946), pp. 121–47. Ann Arbor, Mich.

Hile, Ralph, Paul H. Eschmeyer, and George F. Lunger
"Status of the Lake Trout Fishery in Lake Superior." *Transactions of the American Fisheries Society,* Vol. 80 (1950), pp. 278–312. St. Paul.

Huntsman, Archibald Gowanlock
"Fishery Management and Research." In Ontario. Research Council. Advisory Committee of Fisheries and Wildlife, *Great Lakes Fisheries Symposium, 6–7 November 1952,* Toronto, 1952, Appendix C.8. Mimeograph.
"Why Did the Ontario Salmon Disappear?" *Proceedings and Transactions of the Royal Society of Canada,* 3rd ser., Vol. 38, Sect. 5 (1944), pp. 83–102. Toronto.

International Board of Inquiry for the Great Lakes Fisheries
... Report and Supplement. Hubert H. Gallagher et al. U.S. Government Printing Office, Washington, D.C., 1943.

Johnstone, Kenneth
The Aquatic Explorers: A History of the Fisheries Research Board of Canada. University of Toronto Press, Toronto, 1977.

Joint Fisheries Commission (U.S. and Great Britain)
Report of the Joint Commission Relative to the Preservation of the Fisheries in Waters Contiguous to Canada and the United States. William Wakeham representative on behalf of Great Britain; Richard Rathbun representative on behalf of the United States. S.E. Dawson, Queen's Printer, Ottawa, 1897. Canada, Sessional Papers, 1897, No. 11d.

Kendall, Stephen, J.R. Payne, and William F. Sinclair
"Lake Erie Fisheries Management Plan." Ontario Ministry of Natural Resources, [Toronto], 1977. Typescript.

Kennedy, William A.
Daily Catch Record of the Crewe Brothers Fishery, Lake Erie, 1904 to 1956. Fisheries Research Board of Canada, London, Ont., 1961. 2 vols. FRBC Manuscript Report Series (Biological), No. 706.
A History of Commercial Fishing in Inland Canada. Fisheries Research Board of Canada, London, Ont., n.d. FRBC Manuscript Report Series (Biological), No. 871.

Kingston, William Henry Giles
Western Wanderings; or, A Pleasure Tour in the Canadas. Chapman and Hall, London, 1856. 2 vols.

Koelz, Walter N.
"Fishing Industry of the Great Lakes." In United States. Bureau of Fisheries, *Report of the United States Commissioner of Fisheries for the Fiscal Year 1925*, U.S. Government Printing Office, Washington, D.C., 1926, Appendix 11, pp. 553–617.

Kolbe, Carl F.
"The Industrial Situation of the Great Lakes Fisheries." In Ontario. Research Council. Advisory Committee of Fisheries and Wildlife, *Great Lakes Fisheries Symposium, 6–7 November 1952*, Toronto, 1952, Appendix C.8. Mimeograph.

Lambert, Larry S.
Ontario's Lake Erie Commercial Fishery: A Social and Economic Profile. Commercial Fish and Fur Branch, Division of Fish and Wildlife, Ontario Ministry of Natural Resources, [Toronto], 1975.

Lambert, Richard Stanton, and Paul Pross
Renewing Nature's Wealth; A Centennial History of the Public Management of Lands, Forests and Wildlife in Ontario, 1763–1967. Ontario Department of Lands and Forests, [Toronto], 1967.

Langlois, Thomas Huxley
The Western End of Lake Erie and its Ecology. J.W. Edwards, Ann Arbor, 1954.

Lauriston, Victor
Lambton's Hundred Years, 1849–1949. Haines Frontier Print Co., Sarnia, Ont., 1949.

Lewis, Donald Wayne
The Decline of the Lake Erie Commercial Fishing Industry in Ohio. University Microfilms International, Ann Arbor, Mich., 1982.

Lewis, J.N.
"The Fish Stick Story." In *[Proceedings of the] Tenth Annual Meeting, Fisheries Council of Canada, April 18–20, 1955 ... Winnipeg*, Fisheries Council of Canada, Ottawa, n.d., pp. 23, 25.

Loftus, David H.
The Charterboat Fishery for Lake Trout in Southern Georgian Bay: 1920–1955. Lake Huron Fisheries Assessment Unit, Ontario Ministry of Natural Resources, n.p., 1979. Lake Huron Fisheries Assessment Unit, Report 227-9.

McCullough, Alan B.
"The Commercial Fisheries of the Canadian Great Lakes: A Systems Plan Thematic Study." Microfiche Report Series, No. 305, Environment Canada — Parks, Ottawa, 1985.

Macdiarmid, Finlay, B.A. Bensley, and C.A. Candee
Report of Special Committee on the Game Fish Situation. Herbert H. Ball, King's Printer, Toronto, 1930. Ontario Sessional Paper 1930, No. 54.

Macdonald, Graham Alexander
"The Saulteur-Ojibwa Fishery at Sault Ste. Marie, 1640–1920." MA thesis, University of Waterloo, Waterloo, Ont., 1978.

Marryat, Frederick
A Diary in America, with Remarks on its Institutions. Carey and Hart, Philadelphia, 1839.

Masson, Hal
"Gang O'Nets." *Maclean's Magazine*, 1 July 1946, pp. 19, 34–37. Toronto.

Meehan, William E.
"The Fish Industry of Lake Erie." In Pennsylvania. Board of Fish Commissioners, *Report of the Fish Commissioners of the State of Pennsylvania, for the Year 1902*, William Stanley Ray, State Printer, Harrisburg, 1902, pp. 101–109.

Mersereau, H.C.
"Some Aspects of the Use of Nylon Fishing Gear." In *[Proceedings of the] Ninth Annual Meeting, Fisheries Council of Canada, April 26–28, 1954 ... Ottawa*, Fisheries Council of Canada. Ottawa, n.d., pp. 25, 27.

Milner, James W.
"Report on the Fisheries of the Great Lakes: The Result of Inquiries Prosecuted in 1871 and 1872." In United States. Commission of Fish and Fisheries, *Report of the Commissioner for 1872 and 1873*, U.S. Government Printing Office. Washington, D.C., 1874, Pt. 2, App. A, pp. 1–75.

Nute, Grace Lee
"The American Fur Company's Fishing Enterprises on Lake Superior." *Mississippi Valley Historical Review*, Vol. 12, No. 4 (March 1926), pp. 483–503. Cedar Rapids, Iowa.

Ohio. State University, Bowling Green. University Library, Center for Archival Collections.
McLean Brothers Fishery. Microfilm.
Wheeler and Company. Microfilm.

Ontario
The Ontario Gazette. 1912, 1914. Toronto.

Ontario. Archives.
RG1, HB, Natural Resources, Fisheries Branch, clipping file.
RG49, I-7-B-2, Ontario Sessional Papers.

Ontario. Department of Crown Lands.
Report of the Commissioner of Crown Lands.... Imprint varies, Toronto, 1887–94.

Ontario. Department of Economics and Development. Special Research and Surveys Branch.
"The Lake Erie Fishing Industry, Report Dealing with Representations Made to the Provincial Government in 1962." April 1963. Manuscript on file, Ontario Ministry of Natural Resources, Library, Toronto.

Ontario. Department of Fisheries.
... Annual Report ... 1900 to *... 1905*. L.K. Cameron, King's Printer, Toronto, 1901–1906. (Continued by reports of the Game and Fisheries Branch/Department.)

Ontario. Department of Lands and Forests.
Annual Report ... 1947 to *... 1972*. Imprint varies, Toronto, 1948–n.d. (Continued by reports of the Ministry of Natural Resources.)

Ontario. Game and Fisheries Branch/Department.
... Annual Report ... 1907 to *... 1945/46*. Imprint varies, Toronto, 1908–1946. (Continued by reports of the Department of Lands and Forests.)

Ontario. Game and Fish Commission [Commission to Enquire upon the Game and Fish of the Province of Ontario and the Laws Relating to their Protection].
Commissioners' Report. Printed by Order of the Legislative Assembly, Warwick and Sons, Toronto, 1892.

Ontario. Game and Fisheries Commission.
Final Report of the Ontario Game and Fisheries Commission, 1909–1911, Appointed to Enquire into and Report on All Matters Appertaining to the Game Fish, the Fisheries, and the Game of the Province of Ontario. Signed: Kelly Evans, Commissioner. Printed by order of the Legislative Assembly of Ontario, L.K. Cameron, Toronto, 1912.

Ontario. Laws and Statutes, etc.
Statutes of the Province of Ontario passed in the Session held in the Forty-eighth Year of the Reign of Her Majesty Queen Victoria, Being the Second Session of the Fifth Legislature of Ontario. John Notman, Queen's Printer, Toronto, 1885.

Ontario. Ministry of Natural Resources.
Annual Report ... 1973 to ... 1981. [Toronto], n.d.
Statistics, 1982. A Statistical Supplement to the Annual Report of the Minister of Natural Resources for the Year ending March 31, 1982. [Toronto, 1982.]

Payne, N. Robert
"A Century of Commercial Fishery Administration in Ontario." *Ontario Fish and Wildlife Review*, Vol. 6, Nos. 1–2 (Spring–Summer 1967), pp. 7–15. Toronto.

Peters, John
"Commercial Fishing in Lake Huron, 1880–1915: The Exploitation and Decline of the Whitefish and Lake Trout." MA thesis, Department of Geography, University of Western Ontario, London, Ont., 1981.

Piper, Don Courtney
The International Law of the Great Lakes: A Study of Canadian–United States Co-Operation. Commonwealth-Studies Center, Duke University Press, Durham, N.C., 1967.

Prothero, Frank
The Good Years: A History of the Commercial Fishing Industry on Lake Erie. Mika Publishing, Belleville, Ont., 1973.

Quaife, Milo M., ed.
The John Askin Papers. Detroit Library Commission, Detroit, 1928–31. 2 vols. Burton Historical Records, Vols. 1–2.

Regier, Henry A., and W.L. Hartman
"Lake Erie's Fish Community: 150 Years of Cultural Stresses." *Science*, Vol. 180, No. 4092 (22 June 1973), pp. 1248–55. Cambridge, Mass.

Regier, Henry A., Vernon C. Applegate, and Richard A. Rider
The Ecology and Management of the Walleye in Western Lake Erie. Great Lakes Fishery Commission, Ann Arbor, 1969. Great Lakes Fishery Commission, Technical Report No. 15.

Reighard, Paul Roby
'A Plan for Promoting the Whitefish Production of the Great Lakes.' In "Proceedings of the Fourth International Fishery Congress: Organization and Sessional Business, Papers and Discussions Held at Washington, U.S.A.: September 22 to 26, 1908," *Bulletin of the Bureau of Fisheries*, Vol. 28—1908, Pt. 1 (1910), pp. 643–84. Washington, D.C.

Schultz, Ken
"The Great Great Lakes." *Field and Stream*, North East Edition, Vol. 87, No. 10 (Feb. 1983), pp. 79–84. New York.

Scott, W.B., and E.J. Crossman
Freshwater Fishes of Canada. Fisheries Research Board of Canada, Ottawa, 1973. Fisheries Research Board of Canada, Bulletin 184.

Sinclair, William F.
The Federal Small Craft Harbours Program on Lake Erie: The Socio-Economic Need for the Program and its Potential for Success. Small Craft Harbours Branch, Fisheries and Marine Service, Dept. of Fisheries and the Environment, [Ottawa], 1978.

Smith, Hugh M.
"Report on the Fisheries of Lake Ontario." *Bulletin of the United States Fish Commission for 1890*, Vol. 10 (1891), pp. 177–215. Washington, D.C.

Smith, Hugh M., and Merwin-Marie Snell, comp.
"[Review of the] Fisheries of the Great Lakes in 1885.... Introduction and Description of Fishing Vessels and Boats by J.W. Collins." In United States. Commission of Fish and Fisheries, *Report of the Commissioner for 1887*, U.S. Government Printing Office, Washington, D.C., 1891, Appendix 1, pp. 1–333.

Stansby, Maurice Earl
Industrial Fishery Technology; A Survey of Methods for Domestic Harvesting, Preservation, and Processing of Fish Used for Food and for Industrial Products. Reinhold, New York, 1963.

Talhelm, Daniel R., et al.
Current Estimates of Great Lakes Fisheries Values: 1979 Status Report. Great Lakes Fishery Commission, Ann Arbor, 1979.

Tiessen, Ronald
"The Delaurier House — Family Study, Point Pelee." Manuscript on file, Environment Canada, Canadian Parks Service, Ontario Regional Office, Cornwall, 1979. (Now reproduced in Microfiche Report Series, No. 8, Parks Canada, Ottawa, 1979.)

Times **(New York)**
"Fishery Interests Combine." 22 June 1898, p. 10.
"The New Fishery Trust." 2 Oct. 1898, p. 5.

Tomkins, F.T.
"The Life History and Reproduction of Georgian Bay Lake Trout, with Some Notes on the Commercial Fishery." MA thesis, University of Toronto, Toronto, 1951.

Toner, G.C.
"The Great Lakes Fisheries: Unheeded Depletion." *Canadian Forum*, Vol. 19, No. 224 (Sept. 1939), pp. 178–80. Toronto.

Tressler, Donald K., and James M. Lemon with Alexander E. Alexander et al.
Marine Products of Commerce; Their Acquisition, Handling, Biological Aspects, and the Science and Technology of their Preparation and Preservation. 2nd ed. rev. Book Division, Reinhold, New York, 1951.

Triggs, Charles W.
"The Problem of Getting our Fish to the Customer. Distribution." *Fishing Gazette*, Vol. 52, No. 7, Annual Review Number (1935), pp. 100, 103–104. New York.

United States. General Accounting Office. Comptroller General of the United States.
The U.S. Great Lakes Commercial Fishing Industry — Past, Present and Potential: Report to Congress by the Comptroller General of the United States. United States Government Printing Office, Washington, D.C., 1977.

United States. Tariff Commission.
Lake Fish: A Study of the Trade Between the United States and Canada in Fresh-Water Fish with Cost of Production Data. United States Government Printing Office, Washington, D.C., 1927. Tariff Information Series, No. 36.
Report to the United States Senate on Nets and Netting and Other Fishing Gear.... U.S. Government Printing Office, Washington, D.C., 1937. U.S. Tariff Commission Report No. 117, Second Series.

United States. Treasury Department.
Communication from the Secretary of the Treasury, Transmitting ... the Report of Israel D. Andrews on the Trade and Commerce of the British North American Colonies and Upon the Trade of the Great Lakes and Rivers.... R. Armstrong, printer, Washington, D.C., 1853. 32nd U.S. Congress, 1st Sess., Senate Executive Document No. 112. Serial No. 622-623.

Upper Canada
Statutes. Imprint varies, 1807–40.

Urquhart, M.C., and K.A.H. Buckley
Historical Statistics of Canada. Macmillan, Toronto, 1965.

Van Oosten, John
"Michigan's Commercial Fisheries of the Great Lakes." *Michigan History Magazine*, Vol. 22, No. 1 (Winter 1938), pp. 3–39. Lansing.

Van West, John Jacob
"The Independent Fishermen in the Port Dover Fishing Industry: A Case Study of Their Production and Market Relations." PhD thesis, University of Toronto, Toronto, 1983.

Weiler, John M.
"Michipicoten: Hudson's Bay Company Post, 1821–1904." In *Three Heritage Studies on the History of the HBC Michipicoten Post and on the Archaeology of the North Pickering Area*, ed. David Skene Melvin, Historical Planning and Research Branch, Ontario Ministry of Culture and Recreation, Toronto, 1980, pp. 1–64.

Wellington, I.M., and C.C. James
"Presqu'isle." *Ontario Historical Society, Papers and Records*, Vol. 5 (1904), pp. 61–76. Toronto.

Whillans, Tom H.
"Fish Community Transformation in Three Bays within the Lower Great Lakes." MA thesis, Department of Geography, University of Toronto, Toronto, 1977.

Whitcher, W.F.
"Practical Results of Fish Culture in the Dominion of Canada." *Forest and Stream*, Vol. 20, No. 21 (21 June 1883), p. 408. New York.

Wightman, William Robert
Forever on the Fringe: Six Studies in the Development of Manitoulin Island.
University of Toronto Press, Toronto, 1982.

Woodland, G. Bruce
"The Fisheries Research Board of Canada." *Fisheries Council of Canada, Annual Review* (1967), pp. 53–55. Montreal.